King of the Colorado

The Story of Cass Hite

Southeast Utah's Legendary
Explorer, Prospector and Pioneer

By

Tom McCourt

© 2012

Published by Southpaw Publications, Price, Utah.
Printed by Press Media, Provo, Utah.
Edited by Elizabeth A. Green – The Write Connection
Cover design by Tom McCourt

ISBN: 978-0-9741568-4-2
Library of Congress Control Number: 2012920821

To my Grandfather
J.L. Winn

The man who introduced me to the desert
and told me the Cass Hite stories when I was a boy

Cass Hite about 1890. He signed the portrait using his Navajo name.
Courtesy of the Utah State Historical Society

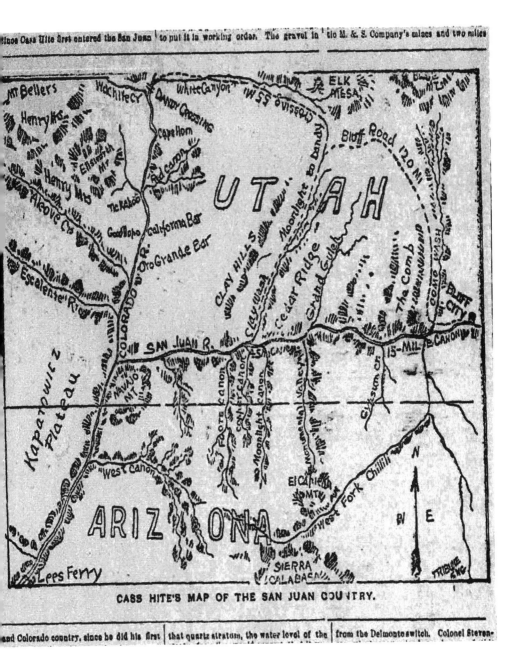

CASS HITE'S MAP OF THE SAN JUAN COUNTRY.

Cass Hite's hand-drawn map of Southeast Utah from The Salt lake Tribune, January 12, 1893. The map covers the area of his explorations, discoveries and placer mining operations between 1879 and 1914.

Contents:

1. Hoskininni's Silver - 10
2. Undefeated - 12
3. Across the River - 15
4. The Valley of Tears - 19
5. Into the Wilderness Dream - 20
6. Moonlight Canyon - 24
7. Hosteen Pish-la-ki - 30
8. The Spaniard's Yellow Gold - 37
9. Dandy Crossing - 41
10. The Wild Man of Swett Canyon - 44
11. The Lay of the Land - 47
12. Wonders of the Desert - 50
13. The Fight at Soldier Crossing - 55
14. Gold Rush in Glen Canyon - 62
15. King of the Colorado - 66
16. The Mormon Question - 71
17. The Angel of Mercy - 72
18. Mining Men's Pockets - 78
19. Unjustified Justifiable Homicide - 83
20. Cass Hite Brought Hither - 87
21. Liars, Lawyers and a Lack of Luck - 90
22. Keep the Home Fires Burning - 94
23. Enoch Davis and the Lost Rhodes Mine - 97
24. Expedition to the Uintahs - 103
25. Fools Gold - 114
26. The Salt Lake City Gold Rush - 117
27. The Long Road back to Dandy Crossing - 122
28. The Beauty of the Mountains - 126
29. Medicine Man - 130
30. Stanton's Folly - 132
31. Maggie May - 137
32. The Bank of Ticaboo - 139
33. Old Dogs Still Bite - 143
34. The Ghosts of Glen Canyon - 144
35. The Trail for Sixty Snows - 153
36. Epilogue - 164

Preface:

The desert of upper Glen Canyon was my special, peaceful place when I was a boy. The sky was bluer there than anywhere else and the red ledges and billowing white clouds made every day an adventure in paradise. But somehow, even as a child, I could feel an anxious restlessness in the stillness of the canyons. There were ghosts in Glen Canyon.

First, there were Indian ruins everywhere and they beckoned me. Cliff dwellings fired my imagination and took me on many adventures in the canyon rims behind my grandmother's house near the old town of White Canyon. And just across the river, at Hite, sat the remains of an old abandoned log cabin. Every time we passed the place my grandfather would say, "That's Cass Hite's old cabin. He was the first white man to settle here."

The first white man to settle here. How those words filled me with wonder. What would it be like to be the first pioneer to see such a wild and beautiful place?

This book tells the story. It is a recitation of history, but a great adventure, too. Cass Hite embodied the American frontier spirit, and he was, indeed, one of the first pioneers to see and explore Utah's red rock canyon country.

The framework of this story is true. References and sources are listed. The fabric of the story is a blending of historical facts, informed conjecture and imaginative storytelling that remain true to the history, time, and place.

The dialogue in this book was created to help tell the story in an interesting and entertaining way while revealing important information about the characters and events. Some of the folklore has been added like a dash of salt. That, too, is a big part of Cass Hite's legacy.

There is a good deal of "Injuneering," as Cass Hite would say, on the pages of this book. The late nineteenth century was a time of considerable racism and bigotry across America. It is dealt with honestly here, the way the characters lived it, understood it, and dealt with it. In this book, Anglo-Americans are "whites." Native Americans are "injuns," sometimes even "savages," depending on what is being discussed and who is speaking. Certainly, no offense is intended when these old and insensitive terms are used. They simply tell the story the way Cass lived it. Anything less would whitewash the history.

This book is not the final word on Cass Hite. A lot of peripheral information: business records, court records, government mining records, family, and early history are not included here. This book is a summary of his life on the desert, his explorations, adventures, and ultimate demise in the red rock canyons of Southeast Utah. Cass was known to keep diaries, but as yet they haven't been found. If they do still exist and come to light some day, volumes of new information might be added to this story.

My personal encounter with Cass Hite happened in 1959 when I was twelve years old. I was at the old Hite ferry site on the Colorado River with my maternal grandfather, Lorin Winn, and my younger brother Reed. Grandpa was in the canyon doing assessment work on his uranium claims. Reed and I were tagging along.

We were just passing through, but the ferry operator and his wife were happy to have some company in that beautiful but lonely place. They didn't get many visitors. So while Grandpa drank coffee and enjoyed visiting with the couple, catching up on old times, Reed and I wandered off to do some exploring. We were told by the adults not to go near the river, so we climbed a big hill not far from the ferryman's house.

We were excited to find some beautiful, ancient petroglyphs carved on big rocks on the hillside, and we began to follow the red sandstone outcroppings higher and higher up the hill, searching for others. As we got just below the top of the hill, on a smooth rock surface like a chalkboard, we found Cass Hite's signature and the date 1883.

The inscription was pecked into the stone in an antique cursive style, a true signature and not a block-letter signpost. Old Cass Hite had taken some time to craft his territorial claim marker. He must have been proud. He was there, after all, before most other men of his race and generation knew there was such a place.

From the inscription we could look down on the quiet river valley that he loved, the ruins of his old log cabin and farm, the Dandy Crossing of the Colorado that he had named, and the big river flowing ever southward as it had for ten thousand times ten thousand years.

We knew, but didn't comprehend, that this beautiful place would soon be buried in the mud at the bottom of a lake. I had a little camera in my hand the day we found the Cass Hite inscription, and how my heart has ached in the years since because I failed to take a picture.

White Canyon about three miles east of the Colorado River. Cass Hite's Dandy Crossing and the Hite ferry were just beyond the low hills at the edge of the river. His old cabin was across the river. Henry Mountains in the distant background. Author photo

Cass Hite's cabin – 1962. Crampton photo. Courtesy of the Utah State Historical Society. This was the last surviving cabin of three or four originally constructed at the site.

Hoskininni's Silver

The winter sun hung low on the western horizon, rock spires glowing red as blood against the evening sky. The desert all around stretched empty and forbidding. Long shadows flowed from the red stone buttes of Monument Valley.

Two men leaned forward in their saddles, trying to coax the horses to go faster as they hurried to reach the safety of the river. But the horses were giving out. The animals were wet with sweat and breathing heavily from miles of rough travel over rocks and windblown sand. The packhorses, too, were hanging back, tired and footsore, being dragged along by lead ropes looped over the men's saddle horns.

They pulled up on the crest of a ridge to let the horses blow, and sat twisted in their saddles, looking back anxiously along the tracks they had made in the soft desert floor. Soon, the older man spoke.

"Damn it, Ernie, there they are! They're just across that big wash over there and still a comin' fast. Those red devils are gonna catch us fer shor!"

"We might reach the river if we let 'em have the packhorses," the younger man said, quick and fretful. "That might slow 'em down."

"Cut 'em loose," the older man commanded, throwing down his lead rope. He then turned and spurred his horse off the backside of the hill, not bothering to look back. The younger man quickly followed, spurring desperately and slapping his weary horse on the rump with a braided leather quirt. The packhorses followed obediently, then quit and turned away as they realized they were no longer being led.

The Indians came over the rise a short time later, about a dozen of them, painted for war with weapons at the ready. Their horses, too, were breathing heavily and dripping with foam. The Indians stopped only for a moment to look at the packhorses. The old chief smiled, then pointed at the tracks heading north across the valley. The men were what they were after. Any fool would know that the packhorses could easily be found and rounded up in the morning.

Young Ernest Mitchell tried desperately to keep up with his fleeing companion, but his horse was failing fast. He beat the animal without mercy, trying to force him to go faster, but the faithful old cow pony was beginning to stagger and stumble and finally he went down in a heap, the air whistling from his nostrils as his eyeballs rolled back.

Mitchell scrambled to his feet and screamed at his partner who was a hundred yards ahead, still going for the river at a pretty good lope. The terror in Mitchell's scream came to the man over the clomping hooves and labored wheezing of his running horse.

James Merrick pulled his horse to a stop and sat looking back. His young friend screamed at him a second time, a sobbing, pleading, "Come help me, Jim!" As Merrick watched, the young man began running toward him with arms outstretched in a desperate plea of helplessness. The older man hesitated for a moment, weighing both the odds and the consequences. Then he started back to help his friend.

Merrick was trying to help the younger man up behind him on the saddle when the bullet struck him in the belly. The boys didn't hear it coming. There was a smack, a grunt from deep down in the man's guts, and the horse bolted and started away. Merrick stayed with the horse, hanging onto the saddle with both hands, but he was all humped-over like he was broken in half. Young Mitchell fell backwards in the dirt, then jumped up and ran after the fleeing horse and rider, trying to catch up.

Bullets zipped past the young man's head and splashed in the sand in front of him. He turned to face the Indians. Desperate and in shock, he started back toward them with both hands high in the air, palms open to show that he held no weapon, and he began to shout, "Ticaboo, Ticaboo, I'm a friend, Mormonee, Ticaboo, I'm a friend." The next bullet broke his knee. The one after that knocked him backwards on the ground.

The old chief and half a dozen warriors stopped to check the body. The rest of them rode on past, following the trail of the gut-shot man and worn-out horse in the fading light of the winter's sunset. The Indians took what they wanted from the white man's clothing, then mutilated the corpse so he would never be able to take revenge in the afterlife. They then went over to the young man's dying horse, still breathing his last into the dusty sand. They opened the saddlebags and found what they were looking for, half-a-dozen small canvas bags filled with pure silver nuggets.

The old chief nodded, then stood and held his arms out in grateful salutation to the setting sun. These were indeed the men they were after, those wretched, evil white men who had invaded the Navajo country and found Hoskininni's silver.

Undefeated

Dineh, the Navajo people, came to this fourth world in that long ago time when creation was new. The spirit people gave them the red desert as a homeland. No other nation was given a land as beautiful or as varied. The canyons, mountains, rivers and warm red soil sustained them and fed them spiritually as well as physically. The people were happy there. They called their land, Dinetah.

But things were not always as they should be. The Navajos were often in conflict with their neighbors. Though semi-sedentary farmers and herdsmen, they were also warriors and raiders of the highest order. They fought with everyone: Spaniards, Utes, Hopis, Mexicans, and Americans. By the early 1860s the Americans were tired of it. Pioneer farmers and ranchers in Utah, Colorado, New Mexico, and Arizona were demanding protection by the federal and territorial governments.

The American Civil War was raging in the East, but President Abraham Lincoln sent federal troops to protect the frontier. Former mountain man Kit Carson was commissioned a Lieutenant Colonel in the Union Army and sent to the Navajo country. He took with him a battalion of cavalry to subdue and discipline the pirates of the desert.

Carson employed Ute mercenaries as scouts and advisors. The Southern Utes had been enemies of the Navajos for a long time and they were eager for a fight. They did their job well. The Navajos feared the Utes more than they feared the blue coat soldiers. Utes fought like Navajos and they thought like Navajos. With the rifles and cannons of the American army backing them up, the Utes scoured the dark canyons and hidden mesa tops to put the fear of God into their old enemies.

Carson was brutal. He employed scorched earth tactics to starve the Navajos into submission. He shot their horses and sheep, burned their homes, trampled their gardens and chopped down their fruit trees. In 1863 Carson rounded up the defeated and starving Navajos and marched them to a government concentration camp at Bosque Redondo - Fort Sumner - New Mexico. Only a few hundred escaped by scattering in small groups and hiding in remote hills and canyons.

Five years later the warrior spirit had been purged from the 8,500 detainees. Many had died from bad water, bad food, bad management by government agents and raids on the prison farms by neighboring Comanches. In 1868 the humbled, gaunt, and poverty-stricken Navajos were allowed to return to their ancestral homeland to reclaim the ruins of their farms and former lives. They were given the land by treaty and promised that if they gave up their warrior ways and stayed in their own territory, the white people would leave them alone.

One of the holdouts who never surrendered to the soldiers was a warrior the Indians called Hush-Kaaney, meaning "the angry one." An anglicized version of his name is recorded in the history books. The white people called him Hoskininni.

Hoskininni and his family of about twenty people, including plural wives and children, escaped to the uninhabited regions near Navajo Mountain and hid there for six years. Initially, the threat of starvation was very real. Hoskininni pushed his people relentlessly, prodding them continually to gather wild plants, nuts, and grass seeds to sustain them through the long winter months. He had an old rifle but no bullets, so the family hunted in the old way, with traps, snares, and flint-tipped arrows. The family never went to a trading post during the time of their hiding. They made what they needed or did without.

Under Hoskininni's leadership things steadily improved for his little band of free Navajos. They had about 20 sheep when they fled to the wilderness and they tended them carefully, slowly building a good herd.

After the first year or two in hiding they were able to plant gardens again, which greatly improved their situation.

When the Navajo captives returned in 1868, Hoskininni and his family came out of the hidden canyons to greet them. They made an impressive spectacle for their starved and spirit-broken tribesmen. The Hoskininni family had prospered during their time of hiding. Unlike the captives, they were fat and happy. Hoskininni's people had many horses, sheep, blankets, and lots of silver.

Hoskininni became a legend and an inspiring leader among the Navajo people. He was the one who had defied the soldiers and risked starvation to stay in his own country. He had lived the old ways, like his grandfathers, and his sacrifices had made him rich. Yet he was generous and shared his wealth with his kinsmen and others of the tribe.

The Navajos wanted to know how Hoskininni had acquired so much silver. His family was shining with it. He told them he was riding his horse one day when he saw silver glistening like sparkling water among some rocks. He knew immediately what it was. Before the Navajos faced the wrath of Kit Carson, they had learned to make silver jewelry from the Mexicans, usually melting silver coins to gain the raw material. Hoskininni's silver was so pure it could be worked without smelting. He took some of it back to his hidden camp and began to hammer it into ornaments.

Later he returned to the site with six Navajo men and dug silver from the ground, carrying a large quantity of it back to the Indian camps. He swore the other men to silence, warning that if white men ever found the silver they would invade the Navajo country and wipe out the Navajo people, or send them again to prison at the Bosque Redondo.

To Hoskininni, the land was a sacred gift from the spirit people. Silver was only a trifle to be used for ornaments. He would never consider trading one for the other, and he would not allow other Navajos to do so either. As the man who found and guarded the treasure, he recognized that the fate of all the Navajos might rest in his hands. To the end of his life, Hoskininni refused to show anyone else where he had found the silver.

Navajo Chief Hoskininni
Northern Arizona University, Cline Library, Stuart Malcolm Young Collection.
NAU-PH.643.1.25

Across the River

By the winter of 1879-80, there were a few white families living along the north bank of the San Juan River near the mouths of Recapture, Montezuma, and McElmo creeks. They were the vanguard of American westward expansion, pioneers trying to tame the Utah wilderness and make a living raising cattle and corn.

Some of the settlers were Mormons, sent to this inhospitable region by church leaders to claim a foothold for the church on the southern frontier. Others were ranchers, miners, and outlaws who had trickled in from Colorado and points east. It was still that restless time following the American Civil War. Thousands of ex-soldiers, unable to adapt to the quiet boredom of domestic tranquility after experiencing the adrenaline rush of war, were testing the width and breadth of the new continent, seeking their fortunes.

The San Juan River was the southern boundary of white settlement in the region. It was the unofficial dividing line between Utah Territory and the Navajo reservation. The original 1868 reservation was a block of land 100 miles square in the northwest corner of New Mexico. It was expanded several times after 1878 to include parts of Northern Arizona and Southern Utah. The early boundaries did not follow natural topographical features, but were set by a surveyor's transit. Few signs or markers were erected along the survey lines, so the limits of the reservation were always in question. Lacking proper signposts and being more practical than the government wizards who set the boundaries, the Navajos and white settlers of the early pioneer period considered all of the land south of the San Juan to be Navajo territory.

In January 1880, Henry Mitchell stopped at the cabins of the Schurtz family near the mouth of Montezuma Creek. Peter Schurtz Jr. put down his grubbing hoe and walked over as Mitchell got down from his horse.

"How ya doin', Johnny Reb?" Schurtz grinned.

Mitchell smiled at the old joke between them, then replied, "Doin' fairly middlin' you damn Yankee." Then, getting down to business, he said, "I come to talk 'bout the boys. I think we got some injun troubles."

"How so?"

"Ernest and Jim Merrick crossed the river to the reservation an' they been gone nigh on two weeks. Said they'd be back 'fore now. Maw is gittin' purdy fidgety. I think I better go have a look. I was wondrin' if some a you men might go with me."

"Did they go back to the mine?" Schurtz asked with an air of suspicion.

Mitchell fidgeted nervously, then said, "Yes, old friend. They went back to the mine."

"Did that Navajo go with 'em?"

"Naw, we ain't seen that injun since he took 'em there the first time."

Mitchell paused for a moment, then added, "That old buck did say Hoskininni would kill him if he ever found out he showed 'em the location. That's part a what's got me spooked 'bout the boys not comin' back yet."

"Tell me Mitchell, did the boys really find silver out there, or is it just a tall tale?"

Mitchell swallowed hard and put his hands deep in his pockets. He then looked around cautiously, as if he were about to reveal a terrible secret.

"They found silver," he said quietly. "Silver pure as any I've ever seen. Didn't know a man could find silver like that in the ground."

"So the rumors are true?"

"Yes, the rumors are true."

"How did the boys find out about that mine?" Schurtz asked.

"We been tradin' with them injuns for nigh on a year now. Ernest got to be friends with an old Navajo we call Rabbit Ears John. He comes to trade fairly often. Sometimes he trades silver. Brings in rings, bracelets, doodads, and such.

"Well, one day old Rabbit Ears John come to trade an' he had a silver necklace hangin' down his chest that musta weighed a pound an a half. The boys got to dickerin' and traded him an old saddle and a pint a home-brew whiskey for it. They got to pressin' him about where all that silver come from, an offerin' presents so he'd tell, an after he got all likkered up – ole Rabbit Ears loves that corn mash whiskey – he told 'em he'd show 'em the silver mine if they'd give him a keg a whiskey an some a that velvet cloth and stuff."

"It was that easy?"

Mitchell smiled and shrugged his shoulders as if telling a joke. "Damned if he didn't take 'em out there and show 'em that Navajo silver mine. They had to sneak in there, across the river an' all. Ole Rabbit Ears John was scared plumb to death, afraid a them other injuns, but he wanted that whiskey real bad."

"And they found the silver?"

"The boys come back with the purdiest silver ore I ever did see. In fact, most of it wasn't ore. It was pure silver. Some chunks near as big as yer fist. They went back two weeks ago with a pack string. Said they'd be bringin' out a couple a hundred pounds a silver this time."

"Holy Jehosaphat. Who'd a thunk?"

"If some a you men will go with me, I'll see yer paid well for yer troubles," Mitchell offered. "Once we find the boys an' the silver, of course."

"Do you know where that mine is and where to go look for the boys?"

"No, I'm sorry I don't." Mitchell confessed. "Them boys been real tight-lipped 'bout the whole affair, an' rightly so. That Cass Hite an' a couple a other prospector fellers been badgerin' 'em somthin' fierce, ever since rumors got out about that first little batch a silver they brought in last month. The boys wouldn't tell me, Maw, or nobody else about where that mine is, afraid one a them rowdies might beat 'em back to it."

"Well, you'll have to give me a couple a days for Oscar to get back from Mancos," Schurtz said. "I can't go till my brother gets here."

"Come on up ta my place when he shows up," Mitchell told him. "I'll have everything ready ta go when ya get there."

Two days later the search party assembled at the Mitchell Trading Post near the mouth of McElmo Creek. The group consisted of Henry Mitchell, his son John, and Peter and Oscar Shurtz. Grandpa Schurtz, Peter Sr., wanted to go, too, but Mitchell wouldn't let him. "Too many men might arouse the suspicions of the Navajos," he said. But he was probably making an excuse since old man Schurtz was 72 years old at the time, ancient for a frontiersman.

Cass Hite was at Mitchell's too, and volunteered to go. But again, Mitchell told him no. "It'd be better if a good man like you stayed here to watch over the women an' children while we're away. In case there's any injun troubles or anything."

But later, Mitchell told the younger Peter Schurtz, "When we find the boys an' the silver mine, we surely didn't want no prospector like Cass Hite there to see it. Besides, Hite don't like Mormons. I don't want you and Oscar to have any troubles with him, seein' as how yer both Mormons an' all.

There were only four of them, but the search party was well armed and well mounted. Henry Mitchell and Peter Schurtz Jr. had been soldiers during the Civil War. They knew about fighting and military preparedness. When the packhorses were loaded and the cinches all tightened down, they mounted their saddle horses, bidding the women and children goodbye with a cavalier wave of their hats before turning toward the river. A short time later they crossed the San Juan into the forbidden Indian country known as Monument Valley.

The Valley of Tears

The men came back about ten days later, dirty, weather-beaten and exhausted. From her front yard, Mrs. Mitchell saw them coming and went running to the cabin. "They're comin'" she said breathlessly, "horses and riders comin' from the river."

The extended Mitchell and Schurtz families ran out by the corral to welcome the approaching riders. In her long dress and bonnet, Mrs. Mitchell climbed up on the pole fence where she could get a better look.

"Two, three, four riders an' horses," she said, and then she moaned, deep down in her very soul. She strained her neck and looked long and hard, then tears filled her eyes as she whispered, "four men an' four horses. That's all. They didn't find the boys."

Her husband was first to ride into the yard. Henry Mitchell looked haggard and gaunt, his face wind-burned and red. There was a haunting, far-away look in his eyes as he approached the little group of people. He looked neither left nor right and there was no tipping of his hat in greeting. His jaw was set like a man about to receive his punishment.

He rode the horse to where his good wife was standing, stepped down from the saddle and took her by the shoulders.

"We lost another boy, Mother. I had to leave Ernie out there."

The woman looked at him with crushing anguish in her eyes, but she said not a word. She stood there for a moment, supported by her husband's calloused hands, and her heart died within her, again. Without speaking, without crying, she turned and walked back to the cabin. The other women followed with bowed heads and sagging shoulders. Mitchell went to a corner of the corral and threw up.

Young boys ran forward to take the men's horses and lead them to the saddle shed. The men knocked dust from their hats and clothing, then walked toward the cabin.

Later, in the cabin, over a big cup of buttermilk, Henry told his family what had happened.

"We went two or three days over to the southwest there and couldn't find nary a thing. No tracks, no nuthin'. Didn't know where else to go. We finally found an old Navajo herdin' sheep and made him take us to his headman. He took us to Hoskininni's camp. First time I ever met the old scoundrel. We had to go by injun manners and they near et up all our food. Wouldn't talk to us 'til after they got fed.

"Hoskininni says the Utes killed the boys. Claims he didn't have nothin' to do with it. Kept sayin' we was supposed to stay north a the river. What was we doin' in his territory an' all.

"We pressed him 'bout what happened, and he sent his boy, Hoskin-Begay to show us around. Begay led us right to the spot where we found Ernie."

Mitchell got up from the table and walked to the window. He stood there looking out at the river with his back to his family for a minute or two. Finally, he continued to speak. "Begay said the Utes had a war party there and they jumped the boys. He said Ernie was killed right away. Jim Merrick was hurt bad but got away. The injun said Jim died in some rocks further up to the north there."

With tears in his eyes and his jaw set firm, the grieving father continued, "We gave Ernie a good Christian burial and cleaned up ever'thin' there where he died. We didn't find none a his stuff. We looked fer Jim Merrick fer a couple a days but never found 'im. The Navajo wouldn't go with us to find 'im. Acted like he was afraid. He jus' kept pointin' at some little hills out there an' sayin', 'over there in the rocks.' We looked an' looked but couldn't find 'im. He's still out there somewhere. We'll go back an' look again in a few days.

"Didn't find the packhorses or any silver with Ernie. Don't have any idea where the boys had been or where they was comin' from. Wish they'd a left us a map or told somebody where they was goin'. Too late to do anythin' 'bout that, I guess."

Mitchell took his hat from a peg on the wall, then stood in the open doorway looking back. "We lost a good boy ta them godfersaken savages. I hope they all burn in hell. I ain't gonna talk 'bout this no more."

With that he walked out into the bright sunlight and toward the corral. He had chores to do.

Into the Wilderness Dream

Cass Hite was offended when Henry Mitchell wouldn't let him join the search party, but he stayed at the Mitchell cabins for three days waiting to see if the men might come back quickly. When the fourth day broke and there was no sign of them, he told Grandpa Schurtz he was going to go have a look around. He saddled his horse and rode off down the river.

Cass Hite had shown up at Mitchell's a few months earlier, a prospector, drifting south from the diggings around Denver, Telluride, and Silverton.

He was born, Lewis Cass Hite, on March 3, 1845, in Marion, Illinois. The family later moved to Missouri and Cass lived near St. Louis until going west to seek his fortune at the age of 21. By going west he was following in the footsteps of his father, Lewis Hite, and an uncle, Levi Hite, who had been Forty-niners during the California gold rush.

Cass spent three and a half years prospecting the headwaters of the Missouri and Yellowstone rivers in Montana and Wyoming, and the Salmon River in Idaho. He didn't find much, and the climate was not agreeable to him. He didn't like the damp cold of the high Rocky Mountains. He went back to Missouri and stayed for four years.

Cass went back to Missouri to see a girl, he said, but he didn't mention her name and there is no record that he was ever married. When he went west again, rumors followed that his best girl had run off and married another man. A second rumor said Cass had killed a man in Missouri. His answer to the rumors would come many years later in an epic poem he wrote about his life. He said he left Missouri the second time because he "failed to prosper best" there. No mention of lost love, gunfights, or murder.

In 1874 Cass again joined the great westward migration. This time he went southwest, to a warmer climate, to do his prospecting. For five years he traveled through Texas, New Mexico, parts of Old Mexico, Arizona, and Colorado before showing up along Utah's San Juan River in late 1879. He was 34 years old.

He was, as an acquaintance by the name of Ruben Turner described him, "a man of dark complexion, about six feet tall, no fat, black hair, black eyes, a cuss to swear when the notion took him, but harmless swearing, for he was affable, easily approached, good humored, and a man of good manners."

Cass was not an educated man, but he was knowledgeable, well read, and a talented writer of letters and poetry. His only formal education might have been a yearlong stint as a typesetter for a Missouri newspaper when he was a teenager. He liked music and he could play a fiddle and sing when he wanted to.

He always sported a goatee, a thick black moustache, and kept his hair cut very short. Short hair was easier to care for, cleaner for a man living out-of-doors and cooler in the desert heat. His special trademark was a big black hat.

He was a superb marksman, often entertaining and sometimes intimidating people with his spontaneous shooting exhibitions. Some people were afraid of him. As Ruben Turner said, "Although he was good-natured, jolly, and full of fun, he had the look and action of a man it was safer to let alone than rile up. And once on his dander, look out. He wanted action and craved the other man's gore."

Indeed, Cass was not a man to trifle with. He was quick to anger and always carried a gun. The seven-inch barrel of his Colt revolver had been cut off to about an inch in length. Cass carried it in a holster and would shoot from the hip, flipping the holster up to shoot through the open bottom. It is a technique called point shooting, and Cass was good at it.

While not a famous gunslinger like Bill Hickok and Wyatt Earp, Cass did admit to shooting a man in Colorado before drifting into Utah. He also had a dispute with another prospector on the San Juan River and "shot a gun away from the man." After the shooting, the angry man challenged Cass to a duel, but Cass declined. Duels were a thing of the past - blood sport for gentlemen, and fools.

In 1879 there was no town anywhere along the San Juan River. The Mitchell family ran their little store and trading post from a frontier log cabin. There was a family named Stull living nearby, and the general location, there near the mouth of McElmo Creek, was called "Stulls."

Cass was searching for gold in the gravel bars along the San Juan when he became acquainted with the Mitchell family. He heard rumors of the Navajo silver and Merrick and Mitchell's first trip south of the river to find it. He confronted the men about what he had heard, but they denied it. Fanciful stories told by drunken Indians, they said.

He hung around the trading post for a while, watching to make sure they were on the level and not planning another trip to the reservation. When nothing happened, he took his packhorses and gold pans and went back up the river. He came back a few weeks later, just as the search party was loading up to cross the river.

After Mitchell and Merrick were buried and the story of their adventure well known, Cass became determined to find the Navajo silver. He explored the lower San Juan River, locating the canyons, river crossings and Indian trails in the area. He studied the geography and geology of the region and became convinced that the treasure was on Navajo Mountain or a tributary flowing from that area.

Monument Valley and Navajo Mountain were a land of mystery in those days. No white man knew what might be out there in the red rock canyons and sage covered hills. There might be gold and silver just lying on the ground out there somewhere like manna from heaven. Who could say?

It would be dangerous to find out, but the lure of riches was irresistible to some. Several white men crossed the river to find Hoskininni's silver and some were never seen again. Hunting Navajo treasure was risky business. Cass Hite crossed the San Juan into the Navajo lands two or three times during 1880. He was hunted by Indians and had some close calls.

In the pale light of the moon, the three Indians crept closer to the camp. They had been following the single set of tracks for most of the day; the imprint of iron horseshoes betraying the presence of another hated white man in their territory. The camp was dark with no fire, but the sleeping enemy was clearly visible rolled up in his blankets near his saddle. The white man's horse was tethered nearby in a good patch of grass.

The Navajos cautiously approached the sleeping white man, creeping to within a few feet of his bedroll. Two of them carried bows and arrows. The third had an old muzzle-loading rifle. At point-blank range the Indian pointed the big 68-caliber gun at the man wrapped in the blanket and pulled the trigger. The rifle flashed lightning. Thunder echoed in the canyon. Two iron-tipped arrows thudded into the blanket.

Cass was instantly awake. He lay very still, hardly daring to breathe. His rifle was in his hand, loaded and cocked. He was fifty yards from his saddle and extra blanket, his back against a large boulder, his real bed sheltered by a thick stand of greasewood and juniper. No Indian could sneak up on him there. He had left a blanket-covered juniper bough and his saddle out in the open as a decoy, just in case.

The Indians were talking excitedly. They had pulled the blanket back and found only the juniper limb in the bed. They were now confused and afraid, discussing what to do next.

Cass had to make a move. If he did nothing they would surely take his horse, saddle, and all of his gear. Then, tomorrow, in the daylight, they would come back and hunt him down like a rabbit. He couldn't let that happen. There might be a dozen of them, but it didn't matter now. He had to do something bold and decisive, or die.

He could see the dark shadows of the Indians in the moonlight. He couldn't see the sights of his rifle, but he aimed the barrel as best he could and pulled the trigger. The rifle barked and one of the Indians screamed. Cass kept shooting, BAM, BAM, BAM, BAM, BAM. As the Indians ran, one stumbled and rolled on the ground before regaining his feet to keep going. Cass kept shooting in the direction of the fleeing hostiles. His model 73 Winchester held fifteen cartridges and he sent every one downrange in the dark. He had lots of bullets, but not much time to make his escape.

Cass reloaded the rifle on the run as he caught the tether rope and secured his horse. He saddled quickly and headed for the San Juan, steering the horse through the rocks and junipers in the dim moonlight. He had made the right decision to bring only a saddle horse this time. He was not encumbered with a pack outfit or extra horse to mess with. It would take the rest of the night and part of the next day to reach the river, but he knew he had a good head start. He might have winged one of the Indians, maybe two of them, and that might slow them down even more.

He reached the river mid-morning without incident and crossed over into the sanctuary of Utah Territory.

Moonlight Canyon

Cass eventually teamed up with a few other hardy souls to challenge the gatekeepers of the reservation. It was safer that way. With three or four men in camp someone could be awake and on guard all night, and if needed, three or four Winchesters could put a lot of lead in the air in a very short period of time.

A full moon filled the night sky, lighting the desert with a bright luminous glow that was truly remarkable. The warm August night was almost as bright as day. Gray moon shadows formed perfect silhouettes of juniper and sage across the shining, silver-tinted sand of midnight.

The scene was wondrous and awe inspiring, but there was tension in the air. Things are different on the desert at night, even when the moon is smiling. There is a hushed anxiousness that emanates from the shadows. Somehow, the desert is more empty, vast and threatening at night.

The men were leading the horses down a steep rocky side hill toward the bottom of a canyon. The little caravan picked their way carefully through the moon shadows, probing their way ahead as they descended the steep slope. They were trying to be quiet but every small sound was amplified in the stillness of the night; the click of a horseshoe on a rock, the snap of a juniper twig, the skittering of gravel down the hillside as horses scrambled for balance in the loose and shifting soil. Occasionally a man spoke, soft and under his breath, trying to calm a nervous horse or warn a companion of a particularly bad obstacle in the trail.

They were out of water. A friendly Navajo had said there was water at the head of the long canyon to the west, but they had searched long and hard and couldn't find it. They had paid a good price for the information, giving the Indian an old shirt, a brass button and a twist of tobacco. But the man had lied. There was no water there. Now they were clawing their way back toward the San Juan, dying for a drink of water. They had traveled all day and most of the night over unfamiliar ground in hostile territory.

The three men had been exploring the rugged canyons on the north slope of Navajo Mountain for more than a week. They had crossed the San Juan several miles to the east when they entered the Navajo country, but now, driven by thirst, they were traveling blindly to the north trying to find the river more quickly. It was a desperate gamble. There are long stretches of the San Juan where the ledges tower hundreds of feet above the tempting water with no way to get down to the river.

As they reached the bottom of the canyon in the moonlight, the horses began to surge ahead with some excitement, trying to pass the men who led them.

"Mount up and give 'em their heads, boys," Cass Hite called quietly. "They smell water and they'll take us to it."

Cass stood tall in the stirrups, leaning forward to look over the horse's head, watching for holes or drop-offs in the silver moonlight, guiding the animal forcefully to control its blind surge forward. The other men and the packhorses followed close behind, the horses snorting and blowing in restless anticipation of the cool, clean water.

They rounded a bend in the dry sandy wash and the river spread before them in the moonlight like a flat, shining highway. As his horse splashed into the edge of the shallow water, Cass stepped down from the stirrup and dropped on his butt in the water like a kid. He sat there, soaking the cool water into his clothes, boots and body as he scooped up hands-full of the precious liquid to pour down his parched throat and over his sweat-stained head. As the other horses and riders came splashing alongside, the men dropped down to kneel or lie in the shallow water, the horses pawing and splashing excitedly as they sucked and gulped and drank it down.

The men laughed and talked, but in hushed, anxious tones. Every sound echoed in the night shadows of the canyon and it seemed irreverent and even dangerous to speak too loudly.

When the sun came up the next morning there were saddles, panniers, horse blankets and camp gear scattered for fifty yards along the bank of the river. Mixed therein were three men in various stages of sleep and awakening. All were still wearing damp clothing but covered with blankets. Half-a-dozen horses were grazing nearby, some wearing hobbles, others staked to the ground by long ropes fastened to fetlocks.

Ernest Hyde was making a little pile of sticks and dry grass to kindle a fire when Cass Hite walked over and sat down on the ground beside him.

"Got any idea where we're at?" Hyde asked.

"On the San Juan someplace," Cass replied.

"Got any idea what's the name a that canyon we came down last night?"

"No clue," Cass confessed. "But if it does have a name, I'm changin' it right now. From here on out that canyon is Moonlight Canyon. Did ya ever see such a moon? We'd still be ledged-in up there on that rim someplace if that moon hadn't come up like it did. I never seen anything like it. The hand of blessed providence fer shor."

"I agree. It was really somethin' ta see," said Hyde.

As the men were talking, A.R. VanAnsdale walked over and said, very quietly, "Get yer guns men. There's an Indian on horseback comin' from down the river."

The three men acted very nonchalant, but pistols were quickly tucked under blankets and shirts where they could be had in an instant. Cass stood up as the Indian approached. He raised his right hand in greeting and called out, "Yet-tah-hay."

The Indian pulled his horse to a stop and sat looking things over. He had bare legs, a breechcloth and moccasins, but he wore a ragged old white man's shirt and a floppy felt hat. He had an ancient white man's saddle with a rusty old muzzle-loading rifle resting across the pommel. After looking all around, taking inventory of the men and equipment, he pointed toward the coffeepot and said, "Maybeso you got breakfast?"

"I'll be damned," Ernest Hyde whispered, almost to himself.

"We got breakfast," Cass nodded. "Come, have a seat. We'll share what we have."

The Indian stepped down and hobbled his horse. Then he came to the fire. "You Mormonee?" he asked.

"Hell no, we ain't Mormons," Cass sputtered.

"Cass!" Hyde scolded.

"We're Americans," Cass said with renewed pleasantness. "We be friends with Mormons and all Indians."

Then he said, "You don't look Navajo. Are you a Ute?"

The Indian smiled, touched his chest and said, "Pai-Utah."

"Ah-hah," Cass smiled. "Paiute, just what I thought."

"Who taught you to speak the white man's talk?" Ernest Hyde asked.

"Mormonee," the Indian said proudly.

"No doubt," Hyde laughed. Poking Cass in the ribs with his elbow, he pointed and said, "This is gotta be one a those missionaried Indians from down by Santa Clara and St. George. I wouldn't be surprised if he ain't an ordained Mormon Elder."

After a campfire breakfast of salt pork and Dutch oven biscuits, the men grilled the Indian about the surrounding country.

"Do you know this land?" Cass asked as he swept his arm toward the south.

"Maybeso," the Indian nodded.

"Can you take us to the Navajo Mountain?"

"Maybeso," the Indian said again.

"Have you ever been to the Navajo Mountain?"

"Maybeso."

Cass turned in disgust to Ernest Hyde and said, "I don't think this man understands anything I'm talking about."

"Give presents," the Indian said with his outstretched hands forming a cup.

"I think he understands purdy darn good," Hyde laughed. "He knows those Navajos and where you want to go. He knows it'll be dangerous and he ain't goin' without a good payday. Can't say as I blame him."

Cass walked around the camp, gathering up a few items, and then he sat down in front of the Paiute. Very dramatically he placed a folded blanket, a tin cup, a twist of tobacco and a small sack of salt in front of the Indian. The Paiute looked it over for a moment, then pointed at the silver chain hanging out of Ernest Hyde's trouser pocket.

"He wants your watch," Cass exclaimed with an amused smile.

"I ain't givin' him my watch."

"Oh yes you will," Cass insisted. "We hit our heads against that mountain all of last week and darn near died from lack of water. If this Paiute knows the water and how to get in there, that silver-plated watch is a small price to pay. If we find old Hoskininni's silver you can buy a hundred watches."

Ernest Hyde surrendered the watch, reluctantly, after making the other men pledge to reimburse him for their share of the valuable timepiece. The

Indian held it up to the morning sunshine, admiring the silver sparkles, then he quickly reached down and snatched up the other things Cass had placed before him on the ground.

"I knew he'd take it all," Hyde complained.

"Don't matter," said Cass. "This injun might be our ticket to wealth. Where else you gonna find a redskin you can communicate with who knows this country?"

"What do the Mormons call you?" Cass asked the Indian. "What is your name?"

The Indian smiled and touched his chest. "Jo-seff," he said proudly.

"Joseph," Cass nodded. "I should have guessed. Well, I ain't callin' no redskin Joseph. That handle is too damn formal and disrespectful to Christians to be had by an injun. I guess you'll be Injun Joe if you ride with us. Can you abide that name? Can we call you Joe?"

"Maybeso," the Indian shrugged. He wasn't paying close attention. He was holding his new pocket watch against his ear, listening to its heartbeat.

The Indian took them back up Moonlight Canyon in the daylight and showed them a good trail going out of the ledges toward Navajo Mountain. He rode in front, happily swinging his watch around and around by its silver chain.

Later that afternoon as they topped a high desert rim, they ran into the same Navajo who had lied to them about the water. Cass wanted to shoot the man, but Ernest Hyde restrained him. Something was going on between the two Indians. The Paiute guide and the lying Navajo were talking excitedly in Navajo and making sign talk with their hands.

Finally, Injun Joe came back with a worried look on his face. He said, "That injun say Hoskininni plenty mad. Come lookin' with guns. Maybeso we better vamoose."

"Damn it," Ernest Hyde growled.

"Where are the Navajos now?" Cass asked.

Injun Joe went back to the Navajo and talked again for a few minutes. Then he came back.

"That injun say Navajo that way two canyons. Maybeso come soon. Hoskininni plenty mad. Catch up quick. No talk. Him shoot."

"We better get outta here, Cass," Ernest Hyde said forcefully. "That old buzzard might have a hundred warriors."

"I'm with you on that," VanAnsdale agreed. "All the silver in the world ain't worth gettin' butchered over."

Cass commenced to cuss.

"No time to bellyache about it now," Ernest Hyde said as he turned his horse around to go back down the trail. "I'm goin' back to the river, boys. Come with me or stay here, it's all up to you."

Injun Joe took the lead as they started back for the river. Cass fell in behind him, still growling like an old bear. "Every time I get close to that damn mountain those red devils chase me outta here, one way or another."

They were halfway back to the river when they spotted the war party. Hoskininni was more than a mile behind but coming fast. Cass spurred his horse forward to tell Injun Joe. The Paiute moved ahead quickly then left the trail when he came to a steep side hill and started for the top. Cass caught up and asked where the hell he was going. "Plenty quick trail," the Indian said, never breaking stride. Cass followed closely, hoping the man knew what he was doing. He didn't have much choice. With an old wool blanket and a silver-plated watch he had put his life in the hands of this unfamiliar and untested native of the wilderness.

The Indian led them over the top of the mesa for a few miles, then off the west side into a twisting, rocky little canyon. The trail was steep, rough, and dangerous, but it took them to the river at a crossing place the white men had never seen before. They crossed the river, secured their horses in some cottonwoods and set up a breastwork of driftwood logs. They got their rifles out and hunkered down. There would be a lot of dead Navajos if the Indians tried to cross the river.

The prospectors waited for hours, but the war party didn't show. When Hoskininni saw the white men take the rougher but shorter trail to the river, there was no reason for further pursuit. The treasure hunters had won the race. Killing white men north of the San Juan was a bad thing. It might bring Kit Carson and the U.S. cavalry back to finish off the Navajo.

As the prospectors abandoned their breastwork, holstered their rifles and untied their horses, Cass said, "Well Ernest, I think that Paiute earned yer rusty old watch. Whada you think?"

"Yes, I suppose he did," Hyde admitted. "That was a damn close call. Looked like there was 20 or 30 warriors in that bunch."

Cass turned to Injun Joe and held a clenched fist up in a warrior's salute. The Indian smiled and nodded proudly.

Later, as the men made camp on the safe side of the river, Ernest Hyde asked Cass Hite, "What is that awful smell?"

The men went to investigate and found sticky gobs of oil floating in little eddies on the river. The black stuff was oozing from cracks in the rocks and seeping into the San Juan. It floated on top of the water, and the pungent smell could be had for half a mile. The men scooped up samples of the gooey stuff and set it afire to be sure it was oil, or petroleum, as they called it. It was the first oil discovery ever made in Southern Utah.

A short time later Ernest Hyde and his brother Frank filed Utah's first petroleum mining claim on the site, but the world wasn't ready for petroleum yet. With no way to transport and market the oil, the Hyde brothers failed to keep up the necessary assessment work and the claim reverted back to the government. It would be other men, after the turn of the twentieth century, who would make a little money prospecting for petroleum in San Juan County.

Hosteen Pish-la-ki

It was a typical early summer afternoon in Monument Valley. The deep blue sky touched the red rocks all around and the world was at peace. Children played in the sand dunes near the Indian camp.

The man rode into the camp before the warriors were aware of his presence. No one had thought to post a guard. There were no Utes known to be in the area and the white men generally stayed north of the river. The people were caught unprepared.

The intruder was a white man, riding a good horse and leading two packhorses. The women of the camp stood like statues with hands over their mouths in bewilderment. Children scattered to hide. Men came from the shade of the hogans with weapons at the ready. A hushed, apprehensive quiet settled over the camp.

The white man rode to the middle of the camp and got down from his horse. He walked to the edge of the fire pit and sat down, still holding the reins and lead ropes of his horses. For a moment there was silence. Warriors stood looking at one another with questioning eyes. The white man sat calm and purposeful, his legs folded like an Indian, his back straight with his head held high and proud. His hands were resting formally on his thighs. His eyes remained focused on the fire, not looking to the left or right.

Hoskininni walked up to the white man sitting at his fire. He stood tall, dignified and powerful. The old chief carried no weapons as a sign of courage and contempt. He didn't recognize the white man and was amazed by the stranger's audacity.

The white man looked up and rubbed his belly; Indian sign talk for, "I'm hungry."

Hoskininni stood looking down at the bold intruder in his camp and began to smile. He admired a man with courage, and this white man was showing courage like he hadn't seen in years. The chief nodded to his armed men and gave them the sign that all was well. He then clapped his hands at the nearest woman and pointed at the man sitting by the fire. The woman scurried off to prepare some food. The chief told two young men to take the white man's horses, and then he sat down at the fire across from his guest.

Cass Hite had made an incredibly bold move. For a year and a half he had been frustrated in his attempts to sneak onto the reservation and find the lost silver mine. Each time, hostile Indians or his inability to find water and trails had kept him from locating the treasure. In the depths of his frustration he decided to gamble everything, even his life, on his ability to make friends and influence people. He resolved to ride directly into the Indian camp, look the wicked old warrior in the eye, and ask him where the silver could be found.

A man of such courage, self-confidence, and unwavering resolve, is a rare thing. But, while Cass was determined, he was not a fool. He had prepared for this important meeting. He had spent months in quiet consultation with the Paiute, Injun Joe, learning about Navajo customs, superstitions and ritual. He had learned what he could of the Navajo language and had developed a limited proficiency in the art of the Indian sign language.

One of the important lessons the Paiute had taught him was this: In the Navajo world, a man who sits at your fire is your guest, and it is bad manners to kill a man who is your guest, at least while he is in your camp. And, it is bad luck to kill a man who shares your food. Cass had quickly taken advantage of those traditions when he entered the Indian camp.

Though generally unfriendly and unpredictable, the Navajos were not in a constant state of war with the white men. They often left the reservation to travel to the white man towns to trade, and some white traders came to the reservation. In town they were peaceful, respecting an ancient tradition of honoring a truce when trading. It was when white men sneaked onto the reservation with evil intent that the Navajos sought to kill them.

At Hoskininni's campfire, neither man spoke for several minutes. There was ritual to be observed. The Navajo and the white man sat by the fire and looked each other over, but it was bad manners to talk until they had eaten.

The Navajo was impressed by the white man's dark and intelligent eyes that never wavered when they met the older man's questioning gaze. There was purpose and deep resolve in the visitor's countenance, and though a dozen armed and dangerous warriors surrounded him, he showed neither fear nor intimidation. The old chief could see that this was a different kind of white man.

For his part, Cass knew he was facing Hoskininni, the desert fox, the tribal legend and headman over all of the Western Navajos. The Paiute, Injun Joe, had served Cass well when he told him where to find the old rascal at this time of year. Cass knew Hoskininni was the man who had found the Navajo silver, and the long strands of silver beads and squash blossoms covering the old man's chest fed the fire of greed within him.

Finally, after the proper ritualistic meal had been eaten, the old chief asked what the white man wanted.

"I have come to give the great chief a present," Cass said, using Navajo words he had practiced for months. He then stood up and walked to one of his packhorses. From a pannier he retrieved a bundle and brought it back to the fire. He sat down again and unwrapped his gifts. Across the fire he handed Hoskininni a beautiful new rifle, a 15-shot Winchester like the one Cass owned himself, and a quart-size canvas bag filled with cartridges. It was a gift fit for a king and Hoskininni was visibly impressed.

"You have a son," Cass said in Navajo with a quiet assurance that surprised the older man. Hoskininni said something to a group of men standing nearby and a handsome young man stepped forward to the fire.

"Hoskininni Begay?" Cass asked with confidence. The young man nodded and Cass handed him a Colt revolver and a box of cartridges. The gun wasn't new, showing obvious signs of wear, but to a twenty-year-old warrior still trying to win a wife, it was a treasure. The proud young man walked back to his companions who quickly gathered around to touch and admire the marvelous new weapon.

Cass then handed Hoskininni some silk handkerchiefs and a few yards of bright velvet cloth, and said in practiced Navajo, "For your wives."

The gifts had the desired effect.

Cass then told Hoskininni, the best he could, that he too had fought the blue coat soldiers and never surrendered, just like Hoskininni. He said he was proud of Hoskininni for not giving up and becoming a prisoner of the blue coats.

He said that he, Cass Hite, had fought on the side of the gray coat soldiers in the big war between the white brothers. He had killed many blue coat soldiers, but the blue coats had conquered his land too, and taken his people captive. He, Cass Hite, had fled to the hills and never surrendered, just like Hoskininni. He said he had brought Hoskininni a new rifle to use if the blue coat soldiers ever did come back to the Navajo land. He said he would stand with Hoskininni to fight the blue coat soldiers if it ever happened. He, Cass Hite, hated blue coat soldiers, just like Hoskininni.

It was a great story to tell to win the old chief's favor. But it was a lie. A rumor followed Cass for years that he had been a member of Quantrill's Raiders, and the story he told Hoskininni that day might have been the source of that rumor. Quantrill's Raiders was a band of quasi-military, Confederate guerrilla fighters from Missouri who spawned the likes of Jesse James and Cole Younger. The Union Army considered Captain Quantrill's "bushwhackers" to be nothing more than criminals. The group disbanded at the end of the war without ever surrendering, afraid they might be hanged for war crimes. There is no evidence that Cass Hite was ever a member of that group, or a soldier of any kind, blue or gray, during the Civil War.

The old chief listened to Hite's story in silence, nodding once in a while and occasionally turning to one of his men who was more proficient in understanding the white man's bad sign language and poorly pronounced Navajo. Finally he stood up, reached out and clasped right hands on forearms with Cass in a sign of brotherhood. He looked into the white man's eyes and nodded that he understood. He then turned and walked away, holding his new rifle out in front of him like a sacred religious object.

Other Navajos stepped forward, offering Cass blankets and food. Hoskininni Begay, the old man's son, took Cass by the arm and showed him a hogan, making signs that Cass could sleep there. Moments later other men showed up lugging the white man's packsaddles and horse gear, putting them reverently inside the doorway. As the men left, Cass took a long, deep breath and let it out very slowly. By damn, he had pulled it off.

Cass stayed with the Navajos for a long time and he did win the trust and friendship of Hoskininni. He shared the food, coffee, and sugar he had in his packsaddles and the Navajos treated him as an honored guest.

They had trouble communicating, but were able to laugh about it. The Navajos knew a few words of English and Spanish, and Cass knew some Navajo and Spanish, but complicated concepts were difficult to convey. They rounded off the sharp corners by using the universal native sign language. With practice, Cass got better at the language and the signs.

He hadn't been with the Navajos long before he noticed items of clothing and horse tack he suspected had belonged to the dead men, Mitchell and Merrick. He brooded about it, and finally spoke to Hoskininni. Boldly, he told the old chief that in American culture, those things still belonged to the families of the slain men and the families should have them back. He told Hoskininni it was bad luck to keep such things if he knew to whom they rightfully belonged. Hoskininni didn't say anything, but the next morning there was a big pile of cowboy horse gear, clothing, and even a good pair of boots on the ground in front of Cass Hite's hogan.

Cass gathered the items and took them to Mitchell's Trading Post at McElmo Creek. It gave him a great deal of satisfaction to turn the property over to Henry Mitchell. It was Mitchell, after all, who had denied Cass the opportunity to join the original search party. Mitchell was grateful, but angry too. Not at Hite, but the Navajos. The fact that the property had been recovered in the Navajo camp left no doubt about who had killed the boys.

Cass returned to the Indian camp after leaving the property with Henry Mitchell. He knew he had planted seeds of conflict by confirming who had killed Mitchell's son, but he felt it was the right thing to do. He might be living with the Indians for a time, but his heart, mind, and loyalty were still on the north side of the river with the white men.

Cass spent a few months on the reservation making friends before he got down to the business he had come for. But finally, one starlit late-summer night he decided it was time. Several men were sitting around the campfire, smoking and listening to the crickets, when Cass began to speak.

"I'm a prospector," he said, using his best Navajo. "I look for metal in the ground. All kinds of metal: copper, iron, lead, and silver. Metal is good. My people make knives, guns, bullets, and cooking pots from metal. Navajos use many things made of metal."

Cass let it soak in for a moment before he continued.

"I wish to search for metal around here, on the Indian land. If you help me find metal I can trade it to the white people for many presents for the Navajo. Will you help me find metal in the ground?"

The Indians all sat stoic and silent for a time, as was their custom. Then Hoskininni surprised Hite when he answered in English. "Maybeso," he said. Cass wasn't sure he was more surprised by the affirmative answer or the fact that the old rascal had been practicing English in secret.

The next day, Cass Hite, Hoskininni, Hoskininni Begay, and four or five other Navajos rode out of camp to hunt for metal. They had barely started when Cass pulled up his horse, turned to Hoskininni and made a questioning motion. With hunched shoulders and outstretched arms with palms up, he made the sign for, "what now," or "where?" The old chief gave him a blank look and made the same sign back. Cass took that to mean, "don't ask me," or "you decide." Cass bit his lip in bitter disappointment, then turned his horse to the west, toward Navajo Mountain.

They traveled many miles. Cass led the way, searching for the fabled vein of silver Mitchell and Merrick had died for. The Indians followed along passively, joking and talking among themselves, enjoying the ride and the scenery. While Cass looked for silver, the Navajos looked for pine nuts and jackrabbits. Cass stopped to take a few ore samples. The Navajos stopped to take a siesta or follow deer tracks through the cedars.

They came back to the Navajo camp a week later. Cass had a sack of poor-grade ore samples. The Navajos had a good time. The Indians stayed up most of the night singing, dancing, and beating primeval rhythms on rawhide drums and tin cups.

It went on for a year and a half. Cass had free rein to go wherever he wanted and a few Navajos always went with him. Sometimes Hoskininni would go, and sometimes he would stay in camp. Sometimes his son, Hoskininni Begay, would ride shotgun for Cass Hite. The Indians always seemed interested in what the white man was doing, but none ever came forward to show him where he might find metal in the ground.

It was frustrating for Cass. He was sure there was a bonanza of silver somewhere near Navajo Mountain, and he was convinced that Hoskininni knew where it was, but the old man remained silent. Hoskininni would ride for miles and days with Cass, always friendly and courteous, but never offering advice or encouragement. Cass did find copper ore in a region later known as Copper Canyon, but he was looking for silver. A low-grade copper deposit wasn't quite the treasure he had dreamed about. Somehow, he would have to convince Hoskininni to show him the silver.

In order to curry favor with the old chief, Cass decided to marry a Navajo woman. What better way to learn Navajo secrets than be a member of the tribe? He let his intentions be known, but Hoskininni overruled his deceitful strategy and would not allow it. Cass was disappointed, but kept looking for other ways to ingratiate himself.

The key to the old chief's family came unexpectedly from his only son, Hoskininni Begay. While staying with the Navajos, Cass totally won the friendship of the young warrior. Begay admired the bold, aggressive white man with the fine horses and fancy guns. Cass treated the younger man with respect and made him feel important. When Begay suggested they become blood brothers, Cass jumped at the chance. Better than ties of marriage, a blood brother of Hoskininni Begay would be Hoskininni's adopted son. In the Navajo world, Cass couldn't do better than that.

The bloodletting ritual was held with full ceremony on a bluff overlooking Monument Valley. The forearms of both men were slashed with a knife and their arms tied together with the raw, bleeding wounds pressed together. The brave young warrior and the gutsy white prospector mixed their blood to become one flesh. At the end of the ceremony, Hoskininni stepped forward to give Cass Hite a Navajo name.

"You are Hosteen Pish-la-ki," the old chief said, holding his hand on the white man's shoulder as he made the pronouncement. All of the Navajos nodded their approval. Cass was both honored and frightened. In the Navajo tongue, Hosteen Pish-la-ki translates as, "Mr. Silver." The name was a clear and unmistakable signal that the old chief had figured him out.

Hoskininni Begay - 1939
Photo courtesy of the Utah State Historical Society

The Spaniard's Yellow Gold

The jig was up. It was obvious to Cass that Hoskininni had him pegged. The old chief knew what he was doing there and what he wanted. Any further subterfuge would be pointless. The first chance he got, Cass talked to Hoskininni about it, openly.

The sun was setting behind the mesa and the western sky was filled with fire. Hoskininni was sitting at the campfire by himself when Cass walked over and sat down. Cass watched Hoskininni for a while, trying to gauge the old man's mood while admiring the way the firelight danced on his silver necklaces. Finally, he spoke.

"I have come to find the silver," Cass said with a repentant and humble tone.

"I know," Hoskininni nodded.

"It is my wish to give the Navajo many presents for the silver. I will make your people rich."

"My people are happy," the old man said.

"I will make them much happier," Cass argued. "I will buy them many horses, guns, and lots of food."

"The white people will take our land," Hoskininni said.

"No," Cass said firmly. "We will mine the silver and take it to the white settlements to sell. We will bring back many presents. The white men will stay north of the river."

The old Indian looked at Cass with deep and brooding eyes. Then he said, "Silver makes white men greedy and cruel in their hearts. It is an illness they have. They will come with guns and blue coat soldiers. They will wash over our land like a flood. We will kill some, but in the end they will overpower us and drive us from this land, or put us in cages like cattle. I have seen it in my dreams."

Hoskininni paused for effect, then continued.

"We are Dineh, the people, and the spirit beings gave us this land at the beginning of creation. We are to live here and die here. We cannot trade our land for silver and the white man's goods."

The old Indian and the greedy prospector sat looking into the fire for a long time without speaking. Then Hoskininni said:

"You are a brave man, Hosteen Pish-la-ki. I could have killed you when you came here. But you are a foolish man, too. You seek silver to make you rich. You have lost your way in this world. The spirit people tempt and torment you with silver to see what foolish things you will do. In the end you will walk the star path in the sky where silver has no value. The jewelry of the star people is made of fire and light."

"The silver could be used to do much good," Cass argued.

Hoskininni nodded, then smiled inwardly and said, "You are a good friend, Hosteen Pish-la-ki. You are a brother to my son and you fought the blue coat soldiers. You have shared my fire and my food. But I cannot allow you to find the silver. My men will kill you if you try to take silver from our land. We have made a sacred pledge."

The old Navajo sat in silence for a moment, giving Cass time to digest what he had just said, then he continued: "If you will go from here and leave my people in peace; if you will promise that you will never bring white men here to look for silver, I will show you another place, a place where there is gold in the sand."

Cass thought about it, looking deep into the fire, absorbed in self-reflection and fretful emotion. It was a tough thing to give up his dream of finding the silver, but he realized now that all of his efforts to win friends among the Indians had been in vain. Blood brother or not, he was still a white man and the silver was cursed for his sake. He had never suspected that the Navajo men who rode with him while he hunted silver had made a pact to kill him if he ever found it. The very thought was unsettling.

Then too, what was this trade Hoskininni was offering? Gold in the sand? Cass had never heard the Navajos talk about gold in the sand. What could it be? The possibilities stirred the lustful longings of his heart.

Cass turned his thoughtful gaze from the fire to the old chief, and then he crossed his arms over his chest, promising that he would never again come looking for silver on the reservation.

"That is well," Hoskininni said. "The place I will show you is by the big river to the west. In the time of my grandfathers, the Iron Hat Mexicans dug holes in the sand there. They found gold in the sand. Some of the holes can still be seen. I will take you there tomorrow."

The little caravan left Monument Valley going north: Hoskininni, Hoskininni Begay, two or three other Navajo men and Cass Hite. They crossed the San Juan River at Clay Hills Crossing near Hite's Moonlight Canyon and continued along the base of the Red House Cliffs toward Elk Ridge. Near the Clay Hills Divide they crossed the primitive wagon road made three years earlier by the first Mormon settlers of the town of Bluff, the Hole in the Rock pioneers of 1880. They spent the night in a canyon below the Bears Ears, near a spring of water by some natural bridges. Cass had seen natural bridges before, but nothing near the size and majesty of the bridges near the Navajo spring.

The next morning they passed below Mossback Butte and traveled west down a long, wide canyon toward the Colorado River, following an old Indian trail. It was new country to Hite and he noted the landmarks carefully, remembering where the water was and where the trails crossed the canyon. The Indians didn't seem to have a particular name for the place, so Cass called it White Canyon, after a layer of hard, whitish-colored sandstone that capped the Canyon's inner rim. White Canyon is actually a valley with a deep inner gorge containing White Canyon wash - a canyon within a canyon. The Indian trail was on the south rim above the inner gorge.

They reached the river early in the evening. The mighty Colorado rolled through upper Glen Canyon in all her glory. She spanned all of four hundred yards at the mouth of White Canyon, a big river by Western standards. The water was tinted a reddish-brown color from the tons of silt she carried from carving the upper canyons. The riverbank was lined with willow, grass and cottonwood trees. The cool water and shade were a blessing after traveling all day in the heat of the desert.

The travelers camped at the mouth of White Canyon in the shadow of a high protruding ridge of rock that held the ruins of a magnificent stone building up against a purple sky. Before it was dark, Cass hiked up to investigate the ruin, thinking it might be of Spanish origin. He was disappointed. Pottery shards, flint chips and petroglyphs revealed it to be only another Indian ruin, larger than most, but essentially the same. When he asked the Navajos who had lived there, they shrugged and said "Moki." The word Moki was a Ute name for the pueblo tribes of Arizona.

The next morning the Navajos went to a place where sandbars filled the middle of the river like a series of low, rolling hills, dividing the stream into three or four narrow channels. The horses could wade across some of the channels but had to swim others. The long ribbons of sandbars provided resting places between the channels, making it a great place to cross the big river.

On the west bank they rode south to where Trachyte Creek entered the river. John Wesley Powell had named Trachyte Creek over ten years before, but Cass didn't know it yet. At Trachyte, the party took a rough and dangerous trail along the river for another fifteen miles south. There, near the mouth of a pleasant little canyon, Hoskininni took Cass to a gravel bar near the river and showed him some depressions in the sand.

"Here the Iron Hat Mexicans found gold," Hoskininni said, referring to Spanish explorers. "They found gold where we crossed the river, too, but those holes have washed away in the floods."

Cass could see that the depressions were in a good place to run a placer mining operation. Water could be diverted from a little creek to work sluice boxes or gold pans. There were no traces of Spaniards anywhere that Cass could see: no cabins, smelters, chimneys, foundations, old equipment, nothing, just depressions in the sand and Hoskininni's word.

"What is the name of this place?" Cass asked.

Hoskininni shrugged.

Cass reached out and took the old chief in the grip of brotherhood, hands on forearms, and said, "I will call this place Ticaboo in honor of our friendship."

Hoskininni nodded his approval. Ticaboo was a commonly used and widely understood Ute word meaning "friend" or "friendly."

A dry wash formed the bed of Ticaboo Creek. The water came from a large spring at the bottom of a ledge about a mile and a half from the river. The little creek provided a thin strip of shady oasis in what was otherwise a barren and sun-baked desert canyon. Trees and vegetation grew thick where the red dirt was blessed with life-giving water. The southernmost peaks of the Henry Mountains loomed large to the west but they were hidden from view by the red sandstone ledges forming the inner gorge of the Colorado.

To the east and a little north, across the river, the towering ledges were split open where Red Canyon flowed in from the land where the sun rises. The big river could be crossed near the mouth of Red Canyon, but it was a rough crossing place. The Indians preferred to cross upstream, at the mouth of White Canyon, the crossing place Hoskininni had shown Cass Hite.

That first night near the old Spanish diggings, Cass and the Navajos camped in the cottonwoods along Ticaboo Creek. After finishing their evening meal, Cass asked about the Iron Hat Mexicans.

"In the time of my grandfathers," Hoskininni said, "the Iron Hat Mexicans came to this place. They had horses, long iron knives and guns that spit fire and thunder. Our people traded with the Iron Hats, but they were bad men. They made our people slaves. They stole our women and our food. They made our people dig in the sand for them.

"One day my grandfathers wiped them out. They threw their bodies and all of their bad things in the river. Only a few of the Iron Hats escaped. After that, the Navajo and Mexicans were at war for a long time."

The Navajos left the next morning and Cass followed them to the river crossing to see them off on their journey back to the reservation. Hoskininni waved from across the river before turning his horse up White Canyon to the east. As the Indians disappeared from sight, Cass grabbed his gold pan and headed for the river.

Dandy Crossing

Cass spent a few days working his gold pan in the sand and gravel near the mouth of Trachyte Creek. He was overjoyed when he found a little color. It took a lot of work and he had to move a lot of dirt, but there was gold there, sure enough. Hoskininni had been true to his word.

He went back to Ticaboo and spent a week or more digging in and around the old Spanish workings there. To his disappointment, he found gold at Ticaboo in about the same quantity and quality he had found near the river crossing. It too, was a fine, flour-like dust, difficult to find and difficult to recover. But, as a redeeming spark of encouragement, the gold dust had the prettiest yellow sheen Cass had ever seen. He took that as a hopeful sign. Somewhere nearby should be lovely pea-sized nuggets like those found by the Forty-niners in California.

Since the old Spanish diggings at Ticaboo didn't seem any richer than the gravel bars near the river crossing, Cass decided to set up operations near the crossing. There, he could keep track of who was in the country and who was passing through. He spent some time constructing a small cabin of driftwood logs and a corral for his horses. From his cabin he could see a mile or more up and down the river and he could watch the Indian trail at the mouth of White Canyon across the river.

It was a quiet and lonely place, but solitude and wilderness held no terrors for Cass Hite. He was confident in his abilities. He had his guns, well-practiced skills in woodcraft and outdoor survival, and a good working knowledge of Native American customs and mindset. He also had a few good horses. If a man was resourceful and careful, he could do just fine by himself in such a country.

To sustain himself, Cass planted a garden and hunted and fished when he had the opportunity. The Colorado was full of catfish and there were a few desert bighorn sheep and mule deer in the canyons. Rabbits were plentiful in some of the brushy areas. Antelope could be found in the sand flats beyond the river canyons. Food staples like flour, beans, molasses and cornmeal could be obtained from some of the small frontier settlements, but it required a journey of several days.

The river was the dominant feature of the landscape. All of the canyons for hundreds of miles emptied into the Colorado. The big river created both the wonder and the loneliness of the area with her broken, twisted topography and impassable sandstone walls. The musty smell of muddy water filled the river canyon, and at night the current murmured, splashed, and gurgled as it rolled past Hite's lonely cabin in the darkness. With no dams to hold the river back, the water level fluctuated wildly with the seasons and passing storms.

The Colorado and Green rivers were notoriously difficult to cross during the pioneer era. Deep canyons, towering ledges, rough water and fast currents made crossing the rivers a dangerous undertaking. The country was so rugged there were only a few places where wagons could even get to the rivers. Lee's Ferry near the upper end of the Grand Canyon and the Old Spanish Trail crossings at Moab and Green River, Utah, were the best known. Between those points, 300 miles of river canyon were all but inaccessible to wagons.

The Navajo crossing Hoskininni had shown Cass Hite was near the halfway point between Lee's Ferry and the Old Spanish Trail crossings. Cass recognized the importance of the place the first time he saw it. The site had everything needed for a good wagon crossing. There were good, flat-ground approaches on both sides of the river and the currents and sandbars were favorable. Then too, with a little work, the old Indian trail in White Canyon could be made into a wagon road providing passage between the pioneer settlements of San Juan and the settled Mormon valleys of Central Utah.

There were other advantages, too. Land at the river crossing might be valuable in the years to come. A wagon road would be a trail of commerce in the desert and the river crossing might prove to be great place for a town or a city. In any case, it would be a great location for a way station, ferryboat, and stagecoach stop. It was also a great place for a farm and orchard. Cass christened the site with the name he would use to promote the area. He called it Dandy Crossing.

Dandy Crossing of the Colorado about 1956. The Hite ferry is in the river at lower left. Note the sandbars mid-stream. Cass Hite's cabin was on the left (west) bank. The mouth of White Canyon is on the right (east) bank. In the early 1950s White Canyon Town was north of White Canyon Wash in the willows and trees. The town was gone when this picture was taken. The road is going northeast up Farley Canyon. Photo courtesy of Jack and Melba Winn.

The Wild Man of Swett Canyon

During the fall and winter of 1883, Cass spent most of his time exploring. He had to make sure he was spending his efforts in the most likely places to find the gold. One of the first things he did was follow the old Indian trail up Trachyte Canyon to see where it went and get a good look at the country above the river gorge.

As he rode up Trachyte Canyon for the first time he could see smoke lying heavy near the ground at a fork in the canyon, three or four miles from the river. Thinking it might be Indians; he stopped and got his rifle out before going any farther. As he continued cautiously up the trail, he soon could see a log cabin in the bottom of the canyon near Trachyte creek. The smoke was coming from the chimney. Cass was disappointed, but not surprised. The backcountry was filling up fast with white settlers.

As he got closer, he stopped his horse about a hundred yards out and looked around before approaching the cabin. It was dangerous on the frontier to show up unannounced and take people by surprise. When he could see no one around, he shouted, "Hello there in the cabin. I'm a friend. I come peaceable." Then he started to move closer, whistling an old Irish barroom ballad to make noise and let the inhabitants know he was a white man. Indians didn't whistle and they didn't know any Irish tunes.

To his surprise, nothing happened. Cass stopped his horse a few yards shy of the cabin and sat there, confused. The smoke told him someone was in the cabin, but there was absolutely no sign of life.

Then slowly, the elk hide that served as a door pulled back just a little and the barrel of a rifle appeared in the morning sunlight.

Cass sat anxiously still, his own rifle resting across the pommel of his saddle pointed hopelessly in the air. He cleared his throat and said in a loud, strong voice, "I come peaceable. Don't mean no harm. Just passin' through."

A deep voice from within the cabin said, "Whadya want?"

"Just stoppin' to pass the time of day. Don't see too many folks out this way. Don't mean to bother no body."

The man stepped out of the cabin into the sunlight. He looked like a Neanderthal. His graying brown hair was long and bushy and his whiskers hung down on his chest. His dark eyes peeked out from beneath a tangle of eyebrows. He was short and heavyset with wide shoulders and thick, hairy arms. A nasty white scar crossed his suntanned forehead like a comet. He was wearing a white man's boots and dirty trousers with his upper body covered by a worn and faded Mexican serape. He was holding a beat-up old single shot rifle with the hammer cocked and ready to fire.

44

As he stood there glaring at Hite, a plump little Indian woman came out of the cabin behind him. She was dressed in the buckskins of a Ute, with long braids and a necklace of yellow and green glass beads. She held a small, naked child on her hip. Another wild-eyed little imp, just a year or two older, peeked fearfully around his mother's buckskin skirt.

"Who ye be?" The wild man growled.

"My name is Cass Hite. The injuns gave me some ground hereabouts. I come to investigate it. Who are you?"

"Name's Joshua Swett," the man said. "This here's my place. Don't want no company. Don't take kindly to strangers."

Cass was thinking fast. The man looked dangerous and he had the potential to derail Cass's plans for settling at the crossing and finding the Spanish gold. He surely wasn't someone Cass wanted to deal with on a daily basis. Cass took a deep breath and began to talk loud and convincingly.

"How'd ye do, Mr. Swett? Got a couple a fellers sent to meet me up ahead here a little ways. Surprised you ain't seen 'em yet. They'll be along any time now. You'll soon have lots a company, Mr. Swett. I got a whole party a pilgrims comin' to the river crossin' any day now. Gonna build us a town, by gawd. Gonna make this injun trail a proper road. Got us a preacher, a marshal, and a dozen old Rebel soldiers to make us a right smart militia. We'll soon be needin' some a these trees here along the crick fer cabins and fuel I suspect. We'll be bringin' a goodly bunch a livestock, too. Seen some purdy good grass comin' up this way from the river."

The man stood glaring at Cass. He didn't say anything and he didn't do anything, but his cocked rifle remained pointed at Hite's chest.

It was time to go.

"Good mornin' to you, Mr. Swett," Cass said as he gathered up the horse's reins. "I'm sure we'll be seein' you again when the rest a them pioneers arrive."

Then, turning to the Indian woman, he lightly tipped his hat and said, "Good day, Ma'am."

He slowly turned his horse and rode back up the trail without looking back. Cass was tense; afraid the man might shoot him in the back. With some of the wild men of the wilderness a man just never knew what to expect. Cass kept a tight grip on the stock of his rifle, planning what to do if the man did try to shoot him. He was a sitting duck, but resolved not to go down without a fight.

He spurred the horse to walk faster and was soon out of rifle range. When the tension of the moment passed, Cass knew his lies about having friends in the area might have saved his life.

When Cass came back a few days later the cabin was empty. The elk hide was gone from the door and the place had been abandoned. Cass reveled in sweet success. He had expected it. Most of those old squaw men wouldn't stay around white people. Such men were often scorned for having gone injun. Others had gone so far injun they truly considered themselves to be Ute, Cheyenne, or Arapaho. Either way, they just couldn't abide white Christian neighbors.

Cass might have felt some empathy for Mr. Swett. He suffered some of the same anxieties about being a blood brother to Hoskininni Begay. Then too, just a year earlier he had planned to marry an Indian woman and become a squaw man himself as a way to win friends with the Navajos.

After Joshua Swett left the area, Cass tore down the man's cabin and salvaged the logs for his own use. From then on, he called the upper south fork of Trachyte, Swett Canyon, in honor of the wild man who lived near Dandy Crossing.

Cass Hite's cabin at Dandy Crossing as it appeared in 1932, before it was destroyed. The smaller cabin at left might be the one that survived until the 1960s.
Courtesy of the Utah State Historical Society.

The Lay of the Land

Cass never considered that he might be encroaching on Indian land when he settled at Dandy Crossing. The Navajo reservation was miles away, across the river. The Utes didn't have much of a presence in the canyon country and the Paiutes were a small, weak, and widely scattered band.

The natives said they had lived along the Colorado since God made water and dirt, but they had no legal title. The Navajos could claim Monument Valley because they had a treaty and a designated reservation. The Northern Ute reservation was in the Uintah Basin and the Southern Utes had a reservation in Colorado. The Indians who called Southeast Utah home were out of luck. To Cass and other white settlers of the time, the land was American, properly won from the Mexicans during the Mexican-American War of 1846. Indians had nothing to do with it.

The first year or two Cass was at Dandy Crossing he explored the canyon country extensively. He went down the river, many miles, checking the gravel bars with his gold pan, following side canyons and watercourses, searching for mineral veins and the black sand of mineralized deposits. He was trying to locate the source of the gold, hoping to find a thick layer of quartz or nuggets of gold more easily recovered than the fine dust at Dandy Crossing and Ticaboo.

He traversed the peaks and valleys of the Henry Mountains, taking samples and trying his gold pan in the small creeks and flood washes. He went east up White Canyon to Elk Ridge where he explored the Bears Ears and the Woodenshoe Buttes. He panned White Canyon, Red Canyon, Crescent Creek (North Wash), and the Dirty Devil.

When he needed supplies he took his packhorses to the town of Green River, a hundred and ten miles to the north. Green River Town was at the foot of the Book Cliffs on the Old Spanish Trail. The railroad crossed the river there on a brand new bridge. The Denver and Rio Grande Western put tracks through the area in 1883, the year Cass located at Dandy Crossing. The town was originally called "Blake." The railroad made it the best place to buy supplies or post a letter in all of Eastern Utah.

There were other inducements that made the town attractive to men like Hite. As the D&RGW crawled farther west, the town retained most of the trappings of an end-of-track depot for a few years. By his own admission, Cass was fond of the devil's brew and he could buy whiskey there. There were also a few soiled doves around town, leftovers from the work camps of the hammer-swingers who had laid the tracks.

Rail Yard and general store, Green River, Utah, about 1900.
Courtesy of Green River Archives, Green River, Utah

The trail, and eventually the wagon road Cass helped blaze to Green River went up Trachyte Creek from his Cabin at Dandy Crossing. Then it followed the base of Bull Mountain, a low peak of the northern Henry Mountains, to Bull Creek. From there, Cass followed Bull Creek down to the tiny settlement of Hanksville. At Hanksville he crossed the Fremont and Muddy Rivers just above the confluence where they form the Dirty Devil. He then followed the base of the San Rafael Reef forty miles to the San Rafael River. The railroad tracks were about three miles north of the river and the shining iron rails went east to Green River Town.

The Mormon settlement of Bluff was about 100 miles from Dandy Crossing in the opposite direction, but Cass didn't like Mormons, so he didn't go there often. He was an outspoken critic of the Mormon religion and took special offense at the doctrine of plural wives.

The feeling was mutual in most of the little Mormon towns. Those outside the faith – Gentiles, they were called – were often looked upon with suspicion. Unmarried and uninhibited transient cowboys and prospectors like Cass Hite were considered rowdies, outlaws, and bums. The fair daughters of Zion were not allowed to speak to such ruffians.

Cass learned early not to press the issue. Mormon men in the little towns went piously unarmed, but they collected like a hive of bees when the buzz went out that an outsider was stepping near the bounds of polite civility. Weapons appeared like magic. The Mormons did not tolerate drunkenness, disorderly conduct, profanity, lasciviousness, fornication or adultery in their little communities. Often there was no town marshal, but the whole body of the brethren made up an effective frontier militia. Rowdies beware.

The little settlement of Hanksville was only a year old when Cass first passed through. The town was settled in 1882 when a devout Mormon named Ebenezer Hanks led a group of pioneers to the area, including his own three wives and children. Hanks was 67 years old at the time, a veteran of the Mormon Battalion that served in the Mexican War of 1846 and found gold at Sutter's Mill in California.

Ebenezer Hanks was a prominent and well-respected citizen of Utah. He had been a well-to-do merchant and a former mayor of Provo City. His pioneering expedition to the wilderness might have been an attempt to escape the federal anti-polygamy raids that were becoming ever more frequent in the territory. Throughout the 1880s, many notable polygamists went into hiding, some establishing colonies in Arizona and Old Mexico.

The town site Ebenezer picked was a fertile little valley along the Fremont River known as Grave's Valley. Some say Grave's Valley was named to honor Walter Graves, a topographer for the John Wesley Powell river expeditions. Others say it was named for John Graves, a reclusive old hermit who lived there in the 1870s. John Graves lived in a dugout - a crude cabin dug into the side of a hill like a cave. He made his living from his garden, traps, and rifle.

At first John Graves tolerated his new neighbors, but as more people came to the new town site the place became too crowded for a caveman. One day the old hermit packed his stuff in a huff and moved to the quiet solitude of the Henry Mountains. There, he simply disappeared, his only memorial a whispered conferral of immortality, "The Ghost of Mount Pennell."

After two years of supervising efforts to build the pioneer settlement of Grave's Valley, Ebenezer Hanks died from injuries suffered in an accident while helping to raise a barn. He was 69 years old at the time. The next year, in 1885, the good citizens changed the name of the town to "Hanksville" in his honor.

Hanksville was the halfway point between Dandy Crossing and Green River. It was also a perfect rest stop. There was grass there for horses and fresh running water. In spite of his dislike for Mormons, Cass built a cabin on the edge of town to use as a layover place. He swallowed his prejudices, bridled his tongue, and put on a mantle of polite civility. He made friends with his neighbors and became a respected member of the little community, even though he only stayed there once in a while.

Cass made a cabin in Green River, too. After spending three or four days traveling across the desert to get there, it was nice to have a place to call home. His cabin was small and not nearly as nice as the hotel in town, but it was a lot cheaper for a man living on the tight budget of a prospector.

In December 1883, not long after arriving at Dandy Crossing, Cass Hite and eight other men organized the Henry Mountain Mining District. It was a necessary action to be able to properly and legally file mining claims on the federal lands. The fact that Cass could find eight other miners to co-sponsor the organization, in such a remote area, at such an early date, tells a lot about the prospecting fever sweeping through the Western territories at the time. The wilderness was becoming crowded.

Wonders of the Desert

After only a short time at Dandy Crossing, Cass somehow linked up again with Injun Joe, the Paiute who had taught him to speak Navajo. He also joined forces with a few other prospectors who shared his love of wilderness and his boundless enthusiasm for prospecting. Joe Duckett, Billy Bright, and Charley Fry were a few of the hardy souls who visited Dandy Crossing and went exploring with Cass in the early years.

In the fall of 1883, Cass teamed up with a couple of other prospectors, Scotty Ross and Edward Randolph, to explore the upper reaches of White Canyon. Injun Joe went along as guide and backcountry adviser. Cass was happy to have him there. The Paiute could find water like no one else and he could read trail sign like a bloodhound. Besides, Utes and Navajos could be unpredictable when they encountered a small group of white men in the backcountry. It didn't hurt to have a savvy Indian as a traveling companion.

The men probably took samples of the ore-bearing strata on a high ridge near an ancient Indian trail that crossed out of White Canyon into Blue

Notch Canyon to the south. There was a good copper prospect there, contaminated with vanadium and uranium. It would one day be the Happy Jack, one of Utah's highest producing uranium mines. But there was no market for uranium in the 1880s, other than for coloring ceramics, and copper was not high on a pioneer prospector's list of precious metals. So the men passed it by, still searching for gold and silver.

White Canyon wash cut deep into the bedrock, so the men followed the bottom of the canyon toward Elk Ridge, searching for ore bearing strata, quartz, or float gold in the bottom of the wash. They didn't find gold, but they soon began finding Indian ruins. Little cliff houses were tucked into sheltering shallow caves along the canyon walls.

The men explored many of the ruins. Some were perfectly preserved with roofs intact and granary lids still in place. Some had charcoal and half-burned logs still in the fire pits. Corncobs, broken pottery and flint chips were scattered about some of the ruins.

To the people who first explored the ruins of the four corners area, including Cass Hite and the Weatherill brothers who discovered Mesa Verde, it appeared that the inhabitants had left in a hurry. Many household items, weapons and tools had been left behind as if the people had simply walked away from them.

As word of the discoveries slowly leaked out, the mysterious disappearance of the cliff dwellers became the stuff of legends. The puzzling fate of the ancient people fired the imaginations of writers, storytellers, newspaper editors, teachers, and scientists. In the ensuing years, many theories would be proposed and debated.

The mass depopulation of the Four Corners area has been dated to the late 1200s. Was it caused by drought, famine, hostile invaders, internal warfare, overpopulation, disease, soil depletion, climate change, arroyo cutting, or simply an unexplained orderly migration to a new area? Was it a combination of factors, or something else entirely? After more than a hundred years of scientific study, no one knows for sure.

As if to compound the mystery of the ruins, the Indians who were contemporaries of the early explorers, the Navajos, Utes, and Paiutes, would not go near the caves and cliff houses. Angry spirits lived there, they said.

Cass Hite and his friends collected a few of the more interesting "curiosities," as they called them, but most of the artifacts were left behind as they were found. Space was limited on the packhorses and curiosities could be an encumbrance. Gold is what they were after, not useless Indian relics.

In 1906, and again in 1979, congress passed laws forbidding the removal of artifacts from public lands. All cultural remains are to be left untouched to facilitate proper scientific study by trained professionals.

The largest and most imposing ruin in the area was at the mouth of White Canyon. It was the ruin Cass Hite and Hoskininni had camped below the first night they came to the river. It was a fortified site on a rocky rim about 100 feet above the river where White Canyon Wash met the Colorado River. The walls were over 20 feet square and about 12 feet high, probably standing three stories tall in antiquity. Cass and other early explorers called it Fort Moki. From Cass Hite's cabin at Dandy Crossing it appeared to be a great stone box sitting on a rim across the river.

Fort Moki became the most famous ruin in Glen Canyon, a "must see" for travelers and river runners until covered by Lake Powell in the 1960s. Dozens of pioneer inscriptions could be found there before they disappeared beneath the water

RUINS ON THE BRINK OF GLEN CANYON.

Sketch of Fort Moki from John Wesley Powell's book,
" Canyons of the Colorado," first published in 1895

As they camped at night near some ruins in White Canyon, Cass grilled Injun Joe about the ancient inhabitants.

"Who were the people who lived in these caves and cliff dwellings?"

Injun Joe shrugged and said, "Moki people."

"Were they Utes? Navajos? Paiutes?"

"Moki people," Joe insisted. "Plenty long time dead."

"How long dead? Hundreds of years? Thousands of years?"

"Yes," Joe nodded, "Plenty long time dead."

"Why did they build their houses in these caves and holes in the rocks?"

"Spirit people live there," Joe said.

"Why are the doors of the houses so small?"

"Moki little people."

"How did they get to the cliff houses way up there on the ledges like that?"

"Moki people fly like birds."

"This injun don't know nothin' 'bout it," Scotty Ross groaned.

"Nor do we," Cass reminded him. "But I've been studying the geology of the ruins, and I suspect, by the erosion at the base of the cliff houses, that it would take thousands of years to wear the sandstone down like that. I think we can safely say these ruins are much older than the pyramids of Egypt."

"I'll bet these cliff dwellers was chased outta here by Noah's flood," Ed Randolph interjected. "That would explain the depth of erosion and why the people never come back to get their stuff."

"Too bad these injuns, like old Joe here, ain't more scientific minded," Scotty Ross mused. "They're so tangled up in their myths and superstitions they don't know nothin' 'bout history an' geology."

Near the head of White Canyon, the gold prospecting party and their Indian guide came upon three huge sandstone bridges.

"Been here before," Cass called out. "Me an' Hoskininni camped here last summer on our way to the river. There's a dandy spring a water up that little draw there, and we can camp in some cottonwoods a little ways up this wash here."

The men were accustomed to seeing weird shapes and natural sculptures weathered into the soft sandstone of the desert. But the size of the bridges in White Canyon overwhelmed them. They had never seen anything like them.

"Well, tie me to an anthill and fill my ears with jam," Ed Randolph muttered with amazement. "Do you know we just rode through a hole in that rock wall tall enough to put any building in St. Louie right inside it? That thing's gotta be over 200 feet high and 300 feet wide."

"Yep, she's a right smart natural wonder fer shor," Scotty Ross agreed. "An' Cass says there's another one just like it on up the wash here somewhere. Cass said he bet one a them Navajos he couldn't shoot a arrow over the top a this one, but the injun wouldn't do it. Afraid he'd break his arrow or lose it up there in the rocks somewhere."

Recognizing the majesty and unique nature of the bridges, the prospecting party gave each of them a name. They named the bridges President, Senator, and Congressman, in the descending order of their size. In the following years, Cass and his prospecting partners would tell others of their discovery, but without photographs and proper measurements, it was difficult to make people fully understand the scenic splendor and natural wonder of the bridges.

As time passed, other people would find the bridges. In 1902, Horace Long, a mining executive, went to the bridges with cattleman Al Scorup who had been there sometime in the 1890s. Mr. Long might not have known that Cass Hite and his group had been there and named the bridges in 1883. Awed by the natural wonders, Mr. Long promptly gave the bridges names of his own choosing. The largest he named Augusta, after his wife. The next he named Caroline, after Scorup's mother, and the third he named simply, Little Bridge, not because it was little, but because it was the smallest of the three giants. Mr. Long apparently ran out of female heroines before he got to the third bridge. Augusta and Caroline were good names, but the stale moniker, Little Bridge, fell flat.

Horace Long wrote about his trip to see the bridges, and National Geographic Magazine published his article in 1904. It was entitled: "Colossal Natural Bridges of Utah." The National Geographic story prompted an expedition to the bridges by the Salt Lake Commercial Club. In 1905, club members toured the area and again took it upon themselves to rename the natural wonders. This time, however, they renamed only Little Bridge. On their return to Salt Lake, the group announced that Little Bridge had officially been re-christened Edwin Bridge, in honor of Edwin F. Homes, the sponsor of their trek. Sadly, Little Bridge was having a tough time finding a good name.

In 1907, a government surveyor, William B. Douglass, mapped the bridges for the first time and he, too, decided to rename them. There was talk that the area would soon be set aside as a national monument and Douglass didn't think Augusta, Caroline, and Edwin quite reached the mark for names worthy of a national treasure. He felt Native American names would be more appropriate. Indian names had the proper air of mystery, exotic sounding syllables and ancient pedigree to give the bridges real pizzazz. He gave the bridges Hopi names and listed them on his official survey charts as, Sipapu, Kachina, and Owachomo. Sipapu is the Hopi gateway to this fourth world, Kachina is a benevolent spirit, and Owachomo means a mound of earth. There is a mound of sandstone near the top of the smaller bridge.

Cass Hite fought long and hard to have his claim as being the first discoverer of the bridges recognized, and in the end, he won. He might have been the first white man to see the bridges in the summer of 1883, but he was with Indians at the time and they were considered to be unreliable and unavailable witnesses. It was finally accepted that the December 1883 prospecting party was the first discovery of record.

The bridges became America's first National Monument in 1908 under the hand of Teddy Roosevelt. The official history of Natural Bridges National Monument lists Cass Hite, Scotty Ross, Edward Randolph and Indian Joe as discoverers. However, the names they gave the bridges were never reinstated. The bridges still bear the names given them by William Douglass of the government survey office. When it comes to catchy names, Owachomo trumps Congressman, Little Bridge, or Edwin Bridge, every time.

The Fight at Soldier Crossing

Through the early1880s trouble steadily increased between the Indians and white settlers in Southeast Utah. Every year more white people came to the area to build farms and ranches at the expense of the game and other resources vital to the natives. The government tried hard to relocate the Utes and Paiutes to reservations, but the native people were reluctant to go. From their perspective, the land they occupied was theirs. They had every right to be there. Who was this great white father in Washington who presumed to tell them where they could live and where they could not?

In 1884 one of the last big fights between the Indians and white men in Utah happened just a few miles from Dandy Crossing. It began in early July when a large band of Utes and Paiutes were camped on the east side of

Blue (Abajo) Mountain hunting deer. At the same time, a group of cowboys was nearby branding cattle. The cowboys noticed the Indians were riding a couple of horses with brands indicating they belonged to a local rancher. When they tried to take them back, a fight ensued. An Indian was shot and badly wounded. All hell broke loose.

The fight had been brewing for a long time. In April of that year, three Navajos were shot in a dispute at Mitchell's Trading Post on the San Juan. The cause of the trouble isn't known, but Henry Mitchell had carried a grudge since losing his son in Monument Valley in 1880. Cass Hite had revealed the killers to be Navajos when he recovered property belonging to the victims. It probably didn't take much provocation to pick a fight.

Shortly after the shooting at Mitchell's, a band of Utes looted a different trading post a few miles up the San Juan River. Indians and cowboys traded shots at each other over the next week or so without inflicting any known casualties, but the whites claimed the Indians killed more than 100 head of domestic livestock before the cavalry came to the rescue. A detachment of soldiers was sent from Durango's Fort Lewis to restore the peace. With cavalry on the scene, the fire of hate and resentment was smothered, but it didn't go out. Hot embers still persisted.

When the Ute man was shot in the mouth and badly wounded in the dispute over horses on Blue Mountain, the fire roared back to life. The Indians went wild. In the ensuing melee, two Blue Mountain cowboys were wounded, a wagon was burned and property belonging to the ranchers was stolen or destroyed. The cowboys beat a hasty retreat to the safety of Durango. There were no white settlements near Blue Mountain at the time.

The Utes were well armed. Many had come from Colorado's Southern Ute reservation to hunt and they had recently spent their government annuity money on new Winchester repeating rifles. As the cowboys skedaddled for Colorado, the Indians killed some cows, rounded up an estimated 100 head of cowboy horses and drove them to an encampment near Round Mountain on Elk Ridge. They also, somehow, secured for themselves a herd of goats, a traveling pantry in time of war.

The Utes hadn't intended to get into a fight. They had their women and children with them. In all, the Indians numbered an estimated 75 to 100 people, including babes in arms, mothers and grandmothers. They could probably field fewer than twenty warriors if they drafted the teenage boys.

When the alarm was sounded at Fort Lewis, Captain Henry P. Perrine was ordered to mobilize his 49-man "F" Troop of the 6th Cavalry to go in pursuit of the hostiles. Knowing he might be outnumbered and outgunned, the good Captain stopped in Dolores, Colorado, to ask for volunteers. This was, after all, only eight years after Custer's miscalculation at the Little Big Horn. Captain Perrine found the Colorado cowboys eager for a fight. He left town with between 50 and 90 civilian volunteers attached to his cavalry unit – estimates varied.

As Captain Perrine and his command were looking over the scene of the shootout on Blue Mountain, Second Lieutenant B.K. West, also of Fort Lewis, joined him with a detachment of 35 additional cavalry troopers. This brought the military strength to at least 130, and maybe as many as 170 armed soldiers and civilians. The troopers also had sixteen pack mules loaded with supplies.

Military scouts tracked the Utes into the rugged Elk Ridge country to the west and the chase was on. The Indians were moving south down Elk Ridge toward a rock formation called the Bears Ears, driving their stolen horses and goats before them. The soldiers and cowboys followed in hot pursuit. The Indians were much more encumbered, but they had more than a week's head start.

In the pines and quaking aspens near a spring just north of the Bears Ears, Captain Perrine cached his mule packs of supplies to facilitate a faster advance. He was gaining on the fleeing Indians and thought he could soon overtake them. The troopers were finding worn-out Indian ponies along the route and they were sure they were only a few miles behind.

The Indians dove off Elk Ridge into upper White Canyon, following Cheesebox Canyon down to the north rim of White Canyon Wash. There they continued down White Canyon to a good crossing place known ever after as Soldier Crossing. They continued on up and out of White Canyon on the south side, going for a saddle in the ledges known thereafter as Piute Pass.

As the cavalry dropped off Elk Ridge into the desert country, following the trail made by the Indians, they were entering unknown territory. None of the soldiers, scouts or cowboys knew anything about the country or where to find water. The men had only the canteens they had filled at the spring near the Bears Ears. It was mid-July and daytime temperatures hovered around 100 degrees.

About one o'clock in the afternoon the troopers found where the Indians had stopped at a large sandstone tank filled with rainwater, but there was only mud and slime left for the white guys. The Indians had drank their fill, then watered all of their horses and goats, being sure to water the goats last to foul any dampness that might remain. It was a tough situation for the soldiers. The lack of water was becoming a major concern.

The chase continued down White Canyon until it got dark. The cavalry rested until the moon came up, then went at it again. It was easy to follow the trail in the moonlight. Because of the large herd of horses and goats, the soft floor of the desert was plowed with tracks. As the troopers crossed White Canyon at Soldier Crossing, they were disappointed to find only sand in the bottom of the wash. After most of a day and night of hard pursuit across the desert they were becoming desperate for a drink of water.

Daylight found the troopers on the south side of White Canyon at the bottom of a trail heading over a rim 1500 feet above the valley floor. At the top of the trail was a narrow saddle where the trail crossed the ridge before dropping off the south side into Red Canyon. Everyone could see it was a great place for an ambush.

Captain Perrine stopped his troopers halfway up the mountainside, unsure of how to proceed without falling into a trap. The men took cover from the sun in the shade of rocks and juniper trees while the captain sent foragers out to search for water. When things got quiet, the men could hear a goat bleating on top of the ridge above them.

Joe Wormington, a civilian scout and packer for the army, volunteered to go up the trail to reconnoiter. A cowboy, James "Rowdy" Higgins, was eager to go with him. Indians had killed Higgins's parents when he was a boy and he had been telling the troopers he was there to seek revenge. The cavalry officers advised against the scouting mission, knowing full well that the Indians might be waiting at the top of the pass. The two civilians went anyway. With no legal obligation to obey orders, they were finding it difficult to submit to military discipline.

When the two men approached the top of the pass in the full light of day, the Indians opened fire with their new Winchesters. As the captain had suspected, they were hiding in the rocks at the top of the trail. Both men were hit immediately. Rowdy Higgins went down and crawled to the shelter of a boulder near the trail. Joe Wormington went down, then got back up and started running down the trail toward where the troopers were huddled. A second bullet knocked him off his feet and he rolled into some rocks where the troopers could see only his boots sticking up. The cavalry opened fire with their single-shot 45-70 rifles, but the Utes with the repeating Winchesters held the high ground and poured down a deadly hail of fire. Miraculously, other than Wormington and Higgins, no troopers or cowboys were hit by the gunfire. One civilian horse was killed and seven others abandoned, tied to scrub juniper trees, as the cavalry moved farther down the hill to better defensive positions.

The rest of the afternoon was a stalemate. Both sides held their ground and waited. The soldiers could hear the wounded men groaning and pleading for help. Their anguished cries echoed in the stillness of the canyon. Captain Perrine offered to lead a detachment to recover the wounded and he asked for volunteers. It was a certain suicide mission and he got no takers. Even the cowboys could see that the Indians held all of the military advantages: cover, concealment, firepower, and high ground. The captain knew that a cavalry charge up the steep, narrow trail was a sure way to lose a lot more men, so he did nothing. He would wait for darkness to attempt a rescue.

The Indians tried to goad the white men back into the trap. A Paiute named Mancos Jim stood atop a rock in full view of the troopers and mocked the cries of the dying men. In English he dramatically called, "Save me boys. Come get me boys. Oh God, for a drink of water." The troopers opened fire with anger and haste and no one could hit the Indian before he disappeared back out of sight. Finally, sometime in the afternoon, both wounded men stopped making noises and lay still. The troopers remained hidden behind their rocks, sweating, cursing, and dreaming of cold, clean water. The silence and the heat were unbearable torments.

After it was dark, the captain had the troopers fire blindly at the top of the ridge to try to keep the Indians under cover while he sent a rescue party to recover the bodies. The recovery detail found Indians swarming all over the site. Rather than provoke a close-quarters fight in the dark, the outnumbered detail crawled back to the captain and made their report. The Indians stripped the bodies of the dead men and got away with the seven horses tied to trees and abandoned when the shooting began.

Knowing the Indians had crept down off the rim and almost into the cavalry positions in the dark, Captain Perrine became fearful of being flanked or surrounded. He immediately ordered a retreat while it was still dark. He had no other choice. His foragers had returned when the shooting started and they came back before finding any water. His command had not had water for almost two days in the blistering desert heat. If the Indians got between them and the spring on Elk Ridge, the whole unit might perish.

The soldiers staggered back up White Canyon in the dark, abandoning the bodies of their friends to the Indians and the elements. Elk Ridge was twenty miles away and they reached the spring near the Bears Ears about noon the next day, dying for water. After they drank their fill they discovered their next crisis was a lack of food. They hadn't eaten for two days, having shed their packs near the spring in order to travel faster. Now they discovered the packs were missing. Someone, probably another band of Indians, had raided their cache.

Late the next afternoon, as the column approached the foothills of Blue Mountain on their way back to Colorado, the troopers shot some "stray cows" belonging to a local rancher and had a feast. None of the accounts tell if the rancher was reimbursed for providing fodder for Uncle Sam's troops, or if the dead cows were written off as a consequence of the Indian depredations.

Back at Fort Lewis, Captain Perrine made his report and went back to routine soldiering. He was criticized in the newspapers for leaving dead men on the field, but the men who were with him didn't feel the same way. Some of them came to the captain's defense and wrote letters to the newspapers.

Surprisingly, the army didn't feel bad enough about loosing a couple of civilian scouts to send a burial detail back to the scene of the ambush. The bones of Wormington and Higgins lay exposed to the elements for more than a year.

In the fall of 1885, two prospectors, Cass Hite and Joe Duckett, climbed the trail out of White Canyon to the top of Piute Pass. There they gathered up the remains of Joe Wormington and Rowdy Higgins and carried the bones to the bottom of White Canyon near Soldier Crossing. They buried them there, side by side. Neither man ever revealed if any type of ceremony was observed or if prayers were offered during the interment. The burial itself was a worthy act of Christian service.

Years later a fence was built around the grave, modified and repaired many times by cowboys, Boy Scouts and the Utah highway department. The etchings on the original sandstone slab that served as a grave marker have long since eroded away, but in November 2007, a young man named Logan Bradford, from Blanding, got permission from the state to upgrade the site for an Eagle Scout project. Bradford erected a metal sign that tells the story and gives the names of the occupants of the grave. A proper gravestone and fence were added as part of the project.

The site is known today as "Soldier's Grave" and it lies just off highway 95 in White Canyon. Jacob's Chair, a huge sandstone monolith resembling a giant throne, makes a fitting backdrop and silent witness.

About six-tenths of a mile down the highway, west of the gravesite, a shallow saddle can be seen where an old uranium road crawls to the top of the canyon. That saddle is Piute Pass, where Joe Wormington and Rowdy Higgins met eternity while fighting Indians in 1884.

The Bear's Ears – Author photo

The author at Soldier's Grave in 2004
before the modern fence, sign, and gravestone were erected.

Gold Rush in Glen Canyon

It didn't take long for word to get out about the gold Cass had discovered along the Colorado River. There is no information about exactly how and when it happened, but the news made a big splash in the little town of Green River. The word spread quickly along the railroad tracks to places like Denver and Salt Lake City. By late 1884 hundreds of hopeful prospectors were pouring into the Henry Mountains and the Colorado River canyons to stake a claim and try their luck.

Before most of the gold seekers arrived, Cass Hite had already staked claims at Dandy Crossing, Trachyte, Ticaboo, Good Hope Bar, California Bar, Oro Grande Bar, and a few other less-famous places along the river. He had a jump on the competition because he had been staking claims since he first helped to organize the Henry Mountain Mining District a year earlier.

His placer claims along the river had not been his first choice. He had hoped to find a nice thick vein of gold-bearing quartz, or pockets of gravely gold nuggets. But after a good deal of searching, he had come to realize that those things might not exist on the Henry Mountains and the tributaries of Glen Canyon. All of the gold seemed to be in the river sand where Hoskininni told him it would be.

It was a disappointing realization. There was a lot of gold there, to be sure, but it was as fine as dust on a rich man's Bible and scattered for 400 miles through the sandbars and gravel beds of the Colorado River channel. It would take a tremendous amount of work and trouble to recover it in quantities that would pay.

Like Cass, the first men to join the Glen Canyon gold rush were not actively seeking gold dust in placer deposits. They were expecting nuggets and shining veins of gold-bearing quartz. Most were sorely disappointed. The gold rush received some bad publicity in the first few months.

Dolores News
March 21, 1885
The White Canyon Fraud

The gold excitement, variously known as the Henry Mountain, White Canyon, Green River and other finds, has been shown to be a small fraud. For the benefit of our San Juan friends who will be glad they didn't go there, we make a final mention. The boom was started in Salt Lake for the benefit of Salt Lake outfitters.

Mr. Gross of the Denver and Rio Grande prospecting party, which went to the region some three weeks since, returned last evening and told a Tribune reporter he had explored White Canyon almost to its source in the Elk Mountains, some 40 miles from its mouth. Mr. Goss goes on to say there is some mineral bearing rock in the region that might hold some silver or gold, but most of the evident mineral is copper. He said about ten claims have been filed but no work has been done. Overall, the canyon is sandstone and not a place to find riches.

When asked what he did with Cass Hite, Mr. Goss said the last time he saw Cass he was headed over the hill with an Indian guide.

Sandstone, sandstone, everywhere, but not a vein of quartz. The whole thing was a fraud - so said the newspapers. Many of the prospectors who came to the canyons were angry. Some focused their anger on the man credited with starting the phony gold rush. One footsore and thoroughly discouraged gold seeker carved his revenge on a sandstone wall along the Hanksville to Torrey road. He dated his inscription 1885. It is a blending of text and crudely drawn pictures that express the sentiment, "Cass Hite is a horse's ass."

In spite of the bad publicity, more prospectors kept coming. A mere rumor of gold is a strong motivator of men. The gold excitement would wax and wane along the Colorado and San Juan Rivers for the next twenty-five years. Tens of thousands of dollars in gold would be removed from the sand, but hundreds of thousands would be spent in the effort.

Cass was shaken by the things said in the newspapers, but not discouraged. Unlike the sad and angry men who turned their backs on the Colorado and went home, he knew there was gold in the river sand. He had already found it.

Cass set up sluice boxes near Trachyte and Ticaboo, but the work progressed slowly. Gold dust worth a dollar or two a day was all one man could recover after hours of backbreaking work. To have the treasure in quantities that would make him rich before killing him with the effort, he would need to move more sand and gravel and do it more efficiently. To do that, he needed help. He would need tools, machinery, laborers, boats, tents, wagons, horses, a good grubstake and a big wad of operating capital. Cass began to explore ways to finance his dreams of a golden empire.

He wrote to his brothers in Missouri and told them he was on the road to El Dorado. He invited them to come to Green River on the train where he would meet them and allow them to partake of the wealth he was about to bring forth. He needed their help and all of the money they could invest to help open the floodgates of eternal prosperity. His older brother Benjamin, and his younger brother John, both came west in 1888. Benjamin's teenage son, Homer, followed a short time later.

His brothers proved to be a big help. Ben was an extrovert with a sparkling personality and a remarkable ability to make friends. He was well educated, well dressed, and confidently self-assured. His brother John was a bookkeeper, just the man to keep everything organized, recorded, and running smoothly. Homer was just a kid, but he had a strong back.

Benjamin Hite preferred to be called Ben, and he is often referred to as "Colonel Ben Hite." He might have been commissioned a colonel sometime, somewhere, but his name and rank have yet to be found on the records of the Civil War or the Missouri State Militia. Colonel Ben became an effective public relations man. He was a good spokesman for the company and he seemed most comfortable among the highbrowed potential investors in Denver, Salt Lake, and Chicago.

Cass Hite, too, is sometimes referred to in the newspapers as "Colonel Cass Hite." As with his brother Ben, no record exists that he was ever a soldier, so the Hite brothers were either good at telling stories or the label was an honorary title bestowed by fawning newspaper stringers desperate for a story. To be sure, the Hite brothers never discouraged the practice. Being colonels got them closer to high society and people with money.

As the gold rush progressed, the gravel of the Colorado River became the primary focus for everyone. One good vein of quartz was found in Bromide Basin in the Henry Mountains, but most of those who picked and shoveled the sandstone formations found nothing. The gold was in the dirt of the canyon bottoms where Cass already had claims. He could never claim it all, however. The canyons of the Colorado cover a huge area and there was plenty of room for many hundreds of hopeful miners.

The one good vein of quartz discovered on the Henry Mountains turned out to be the most profitable gold strike anyone would make during the Glen Canyon rush. It was discovered in 1889 by Jack Butler and Jack Sumner near the head of Crescent Creek. The town of Eagle City was constructed near the mine and about 100 people lived in Eagle City during its zenith. The town had a store, hotel, doctor's office and saloon.

The mine sold in the 1890s for a reported $40,000, a tremendous amount of money. The success of the Eagle City mine turned up the heat of gold fever throughout the whole area. The Hite brothers were able to capitalize on the publicity. Their placer claims were in the same mining district and not far from Eagle City.

Dandy Crossing became a focal point and jumping off place for travel all up and down the river. The Indian trail down White Canyon became a wagon road from the San Juan area, providing access to gold seekers from Colorado and points east. On the west side of the river, a better road than Trachyte was pioneered through Crescent Creek Canyon, soon to be known as North Wash.

As more people came to the area, Dandy Crossing became known as "Hite." Some called it, "the town of Hite," or even, "Hite City." Either name was stretching the truth. There were never more than about a dozen people there, and most of those were transient prospectors or river runners who stayed in tents and wagon boxes, or slept out under the stars. During the best of times there was only a handful of buildings. Hite was never more than a farm with a backcountry store and post office.

To Cass, the names "Hite" and "Hite City" had a lovely ring, but he preferred to call the place Dandy Crossing. The term "Dandy Crossing" made his store and patch of wilderness real estate a friendly place. The name tamed the mighty Colorado and made the prospect of crossing the river a less threatening event. The Salt Lake Tribune reported in 1885 that prospectors had constructed four small boats from cottonwood logs and were ferrying people and dismantled wagons across the river at Dandy Crossing. The Hite brothers probably owned the cottonwood ferryboats.

The store and post office at Hite were established in 1889. Young Homer Hite was named the first postmaster. He also worked as a laborer and crew foreman at the placer digs. Mail was brought from Green River about once a week on horseback. Freight and dry goods for the store came over the same trail by wagon and packhorse.

The Hite brothers ran their store from one of their cabins. John Hite might have worked the claims some, but he was more fully engaged as the keeper of the store and garden. The historical record usually places him in the cool shade of commerce. John was a smart man. Glen Canyon is hotter than hell in the summertime.

Hite, Utah - 1891. Cass Hite is 4th man from left.
Courtesy of Utah State Historical Society

King of the Colorado

Cass Hite and his brothers organized, "The Colorado River Placer Mining Company," and found a pool of willing investors in Denver, Chicago, and Salt Lake City. Gold was the fast road to fame and fortune. No one wanted to be left behind. Soon Cass and Ben were spending a great deal of time in the big cities, meeting with shareholders and schmoozing the high rollers.

It was an easy sale. They would show likely investors vials of gold dust from their placer digs and give them assay reports and newspaper clippings heralding the Colorado River gold rush as potentially the biggest thing since California.

Aspen Daily Chronicle
September 3, 1890

From the Denver Republican:
Cass Hite, the veteran prospector of the Colorado canyons, came up from Dandy Crossing yesterday. Mr. Hite did not particularly desire to talk for publication but he did give information of several large deals pending for the operation of rich placer fields near Dandy Crossing.

"Four new companies will begin operations in that vicinity this month," said Mr. Hite. "Thomas Lyle and a friend named Anderson will invest a good round sum in development of the fields about 20 miles above the mouth of the San Juan [California and Oro Grande Bars, both owned by the Hite brothers]. Mills, Haskell & Company will also handle fields 18 miles below the crossing. A party of Denverites are negotiating for the Good Hope Bar [owned by the Hite brothers]. Another syndicate is after the Ticaboo bars. A Chicago syndicate will also, in all probability, organize for investment at Dandy Crossing. The Colorado River is heavy in rich gold bars. I think the Colorado River placer fields are the most valuable in the United States."

Money came pouring in. The Hite brothers had found a gold mine and it was not in the river sand.

With stacks of money at his disposal, Cass quickly transformed from a humble prospector to a high-powered mining entrepreneur. Not only did he manage his own properties along the river, but he sold claims, leased some of his holdings to others and formed partnerships with other miners. He bought claims from other prospectors, used his influence to talk the value up, and resold them at a profit.

The brothers sold shares in several widely scattered mining adventures. A man or a company could buy shares of a single claim or a group of adjacent claims on a particular gold bar or placer bed. Shareholder money paid the overhead to keep a good number of men employed. Gold dust recovered was expected to pay back the investors with interest. With Cass and Ben selling stock and John keeping the books, the company ran like a well-oiled machine. Eager investors fueled the engine. A constant flow of money greased the wheels.

Being a high-class mining executive came easy for Cass. As superintendent of the company he loved playing the big shot. He was fond of wearing a suit and tie, staying in the finest hotels and eating at the finest restaurants.

He was an excellent salesman. He could tell a great story and he would charm the rich city folks with tales of his adventures and the gold he had found. Then, wearing an expensive black hat and his Navajo name, he would act as tour guide and drum major for those who actually wanted to see the ground and observe the fruits of the labor before committing any capital.

Through it all, Cass was selling the legend of Cass Hite as much as he was selling shares in his company, and people were buying it. In the age of Buffalo Bill, when America was having a prideful fixation with all things Western, Cass Hite was a hero. He was a true frontiersman, Indian fighter, pioneer tamer of wilderness and the man who sure as hell found gold on the Colorado. As Reuben Turner would say, "Cass had a way of gathering men around him." Of course he used his fame and notoriety to his best advantage.

Cass entertained some high-class visitors who helped him build his reputation. Cy Warman, a famous writer and poet, stayed for a time at Dandy Crossing. Warman wrote for some nationally circulated magazines and the New York Sun newspaper sent him to report on the gold rush along the San Juan and Colorado rivers. Warman was known as "The Poet of the Rockies," and his poetry and magazine articles would inspire Cass to try his hand at creative writing.

Cass was thinking highly of himself at this point in his life. Nothing can better take the measure of the man than the interviews he was giving to the newspapers.

The Brunswick Hotel in Denver was a busy place. Porters in gaudy uniforms hustled through the lobby with luggage, service carts and telegrams. Chambermaids in aprons and Martha Washington hats slipped quietly through the shadows of the hallways with folded bedding, cleaning tools and chamber pots. Well-groomed men in expensive suits strolled the marble-covered floors with lovely ladies in elegant finery. The place was decorated with velvet wall coverings, fine oil paintings, potted plants and statuary.

A newspaper reporter stood in the lobby, carefully watching a well-dressed man sitting alone at the bar. The man was lean and suntanned with his hair cut very short. He wore a thick moustache and goatee like Buffalo Bill. A fine black hat rested on a nearby hat rack. This had to be the man he was looking for. The reporter straightened his tie, squared his shoulders and approached with his chin up and firm resolve in his eyes.

"Pardon me, sir. Are you Colonel Cass Hite?"

Cass turned to the young man with a raised eyebrow, then answered, "I am."

"You don't know me, sir, but I'm a reporter for the Denver News. Could I speak with you for a few moments?"

"I seldom speak with reporters," Cass lied. "Business, you know."

"I completely understand, Colonel. I certainly wouldn't compromise any business deals or trade secrets, I assure you. I am interested, as are my readers, in a more personal story. We would like to know who you are, sir. Who is this man who found gold on the Colorado and shares his good fortune so abundantly with others?"

"I'm just a common man," Cass assured him. "No one of consequence."

"Oh, but I must protest, sir. You certainly are a man of consequence. May I sit down, sir, and ask you a few simple questions?"

Cass took an expensive gold watch and chain from his vest pocket and checked the time, then said with a resigned sigh, "I suppose I could give you a few minutes."

"Excellent, sir," the reported said as he climbed aboard an adjacent bar stool and pulled a pencil and notepad from inside his suit coat.

"Tell me, sir, what inspired you to seek your fortune in such a wild and dangerous place as the canyons of the Colorado?"

"My father found gold in California when I was but a child," Cass began, using his best formal language and authoritative voice. "My quest began in '66 when I was hardly more than a boy. I came west on my own, following the footsteps of my father. That was 24 years ago. The West was much different then. I found it to be a place of danger and hardships."

"And where has your quest taken you, sir?"

"I have explored nearly every gold and silver district from the Rocky Mountains of Montana to the Republic of Mexico. I have traversed the Great Plains, the grasslands of Texas, the deserts of Arizona and the mountains of Colorado. I have since planted my stake firm and deep at Dandy Crossing on the Colorado River.

"I am told that much of the Colorado River country has yet to be explored, sir. Are those reports true?"

"That country has yet to be explored by other men, but I have seen it all. My trail goes 500 miles down that river, from the confluence of the Green and Grand Rivers to Lee's Ferry. I'm the man who found and named

Dandy Crossing back in '83. It is the only crossing for 100 miles up or down the river. It was a land of many perils when I first went there. It is a settled place now. We have a fine store and post office. The government has named it the Hite post office, after myself, of course."

Cass paused to pour himself another drink from a bottle on the bar. "Care to join me?" he asked the reporter.

"No thank you, sir. I'm working. My boss wouldn't like it much."

Cass smiled, lifted his glass in salutation, and said, "As you wish."

The reporter continued. "I understand your gold mines are in the vicinity of Dandy Crossing. Is that true, sir?"

"My company has claims stretching for 200 miles along the river. There are 500 men hard at work there, at our claims and others. We have been developing our mines for five years and we will soon enjoy the full fruits of our labors. The Colorado River will surely become the leading gold producing region of the United States."

"What is the country like around Dandy Crossing, sir?"

"It is a harsh and unforgiving land for a tenderfoot," Cass assured him. "Only the hardiest of pioneers will succeed there. I established the first mining camp in the district under perilous circumstances. Others have died in similar attempts."

"Are the Indians bad there?"

"Indians and Mormons," Cass explained. "The Mormon Church claims the whole territory and men like me are a threat to their secret institutions. The Mormons have shown great hostility toward me. Twice I have dodged their attempts to kill me. They don't think I know about their Avenging Angels and holy blood assassins, but I surely do. I hate Mormon Elders as I do a rattlesnake. They are worse than savage Indians, for they plan their perfidy well. I have found the Mormon people in general to be of an entirely different character than other Americans. They can never be trusted."

"How did you dodge their attempts to kill you?"

"I'm a dead shot and I never sleep," said Cass with a stern face.

"Have other men had trouble with Mormons in the district?"

"By necessity we have set up a system to warn all of the miners along the river should we be threatened or attacked by either the red man or the Mormon. We can assemble a few hundred men very quickly if the need does arise."

"Speaking of Indians, sir. I expect you have heard of the recent discoveries of ancient stone cities at Mesa Verde and other places in southern Colorado. I have heard there are similar ruins in some of the canyons you have explored. Would you care to comment on that, sir?"

"I have a good many relics of the cliff dwellers in my cabin and I expect I know as much about that subject as any man alive. I have studied the habitations of the cliff dwellers for years and I have concluded, based on the depth of erosion at the base of the ruins, that the ancient dwellings are at least 30,000 years old. I intend to write a book on the subject as soon as my business interests allow. My book will paint a graphic picture of life in the Colorado canyons some 30,000 years ago and will include an original elicitation of the Mormon question. I will also include many exciting stories from the life of a prospector."

"I'm sure your book will be a great success. Would you comment further on your troubles with the Mormons, sir? With Utah plying for statehood again, our readers would be interested."

Cass paused to check his watch, then said, "Ah, so sorry, but I must be on my way. I have business to attend to. I'm sure you understand."

"Yes Colonel, I do understand. Thank you, sir. You have been most kind."

Cass had a smug, self-satisfied smile on his face as he swaggered out onto the boardwalk in front of the hotel and hailed a horse-drawn taxi.

The Mormon Question

"I enjoyed your story in yesterday's Denver News," the man in the expensive suit said as Cass pulled up a chair and sat down. They were in the guestroom of a fancy gentlemen's club on Denver's "Millionaires Row."

"You sure gave those Mormons hell," the man laughed. "You better stay here in Colorado if that piece ever finds its way to Utah."

"I ain't scared of Mormons," Cass smiled as he pulled a small silver flask from inside his suit coat and poured himself a drink.

"You must of had a real run-in with them to talk like that," the man said as he took the silver flask Cass offered and poured himself a stout one.

"Not me," Cass shrugged. "It was my old man and Uncle Levi. They were both there when old Joe Smith got killed and the Mormons were run out of Illinois. They didn't do none of the shootin' or burnin' mind you, but they were there, in Nauvoo, when it happened. Dad told me all about it. I was just a baby when it happened."

"The Mormons came to Utah after they got chased out of Nauvoo," the man said. "There wasn't anybody in Utah then but Indians."

"Did you know the Mormons got run out of Missouri before they got run out of Illinois?" Cass offered. "That was back in the thirties. Ole Governor Boggs set the state militia on 'em and run 'em clear out of the state. I lived in Missouri for a long time and heard all the stories. One a those Mormon Avenging Angels shot ole Governor Boggs and darn near killed him. That sect is filled with holy blood avengers and assassins, just like I said in the newspaper."

"I hear the Mormons are going to swear off polygamy," the man said. "The papers say that new prophet of theirs has issued a holy writ that forbids it."

"Ah, the twin relics of barbarism, slavery and polygamy," Cass smiled. "We stamped out one. Still got one to go." He tipped the flask up to drain the last tiny drop.

"Those Mormons will never give up polygamy," said Cass. "There's as much of it in the territory now as there ever was. They just keep it under the covers better, if ya know what I mean. It's a shame there's so many single men in Utah while a few a those Holy Joes have six or eight wives."

"Are the plural wives really out in the open with it?"

"You ought to visit one of those little Mormon towns on the frontier. A man doesn't dare smile or even tip his hat to a woman on the street. Some pious preacher might gut you with a pitchfork. I know a man who got chased 20 miles out of town for simply sayin' hello to a pretty girl. Yessir, those Mormons are damn possessive about their women. I think polygamy is here to stay."

The Angel of Mercy

During the winter of 1890-1891, Cass was traveling extensively while taking care of business. He was good at what he did, but he was handling a lot of money and he was drinking too much. He would be 46 soon and the whiskey was beginning to take a toll. Earlier that fall he had developed a cough, and while in Salt Lake City during the coldest part of the year, he came down with a bad case of pneumonia. Friends helped him from his hotel room and took him to a hospital.

The doctors did all they could for him and in a few days he was feeling a little better. He could sit up and drink chicken soup, and he could cuss the stinky poultices the nurses kept placing on his chest and around his neck.

The king of the Colorado was an independent soul and not one to take medical advice lying down. In spite of a doctor's prescription for complete bed rest, he decided that what he needed more than medicine was the warm, healing airs of the desert. Salt Lake was too close to the Arctic Circle. Even Brigham Young had fled the place and traveled south in the wintertime.

A friend helped him to the depot and Cass took the next southbound train for Green River. He sat quietly in the back of the Pullman car, chilled, though wrapped in a big wool coat. The train ride took all day with stops in Provo, Coltin, Helper, and Price. By the time the eastbound iron zephyr rolled into Green River it was almost dark. Cass checked in at the Palmer House Hotel and went right to bed. He was exhausted and feeling very weak.

The next morning Cass could hardly get out of bed. His lungs were full of fluid and he felt nauseous and light-headed. He dressed himself and walked carefully to the lobby. There, he asked a porter if he knew of anyone who might be able to drive him to Dandy Crossing. The Green River stage ran only once a week and Cass didn't want to wait for another three days.

The porter returned in half an hour with a teenaged boy driving a buggy behind a small bay horse. "This young feller says he can take you home," the porter said.

"Thank you," said Cass as he handed the man a coin.

"Don't I know you?" Cass asked the boy.

"Yessir," the boy answered. "Sometimes I shine shoes at the railroad depot. I'm savin' my money so's I can buy a horse an' get outta this deadbeat town."

"Hmm, I didn't think it was that bad here," Cass mused, wiping his feverish brow with a handkerchief. "It could be worse. You could be stuck in Provo."

The boy stood looking up at Cass with juvenile disgust in his eyes.

"I'll give you four dollars to take me to Dandy Crossing," Cass offered. "That'll help you buy a horse."

The young man wrinkled his brow. "Dandy Crossing and back will take four or five days," he said. "Make it four-fifty and I'll do it."

The boy's impudence annoyed him, but Cass was too sick to argue. "Done," he nodded darkly. Then he whispered under his breath, "Damn little road agent."

The Palmer House Hotel in Green River, Utah – 1890s
Courtesy of Green River Archives, Green River, Utah.

The boy loaded Hite's trunk in the back of the buggy, then stopped at his mother's house to get some food, blankets and articles of camping gear to facilitate the journey. They rolled out of Green River later that morning. Hanksville would be a full day's journey and they wouldn't be there until after dark. It was the first week of February. There was no snow on the desert but the days were cold. Cass wrapped himself in a big wool blanket and wore his gloves and overshoes.

The kid talked non-stop and it annoyed Cass. He was very sick and he clung to the handrail tightly as the surrey bounced and bucked over the rocks and gravel. They stopped at the San Rafael River and watered the horse, then followed the primitive track south along the bottom of the San Rafael Reef. Several miles down the road, near Old Woman Wash, they got stuck in the sand. Cass had nodded off and didn't see when the kid turned aside to miss a hole in the road and buried the wagon wheels in a sand dune.

The little horse couldn't pull them free. The buggy was stuck to the axles. The kid got off and began to unload Cass's steamer trunk and his own boxes of camp supplies and groceries. He then invited Cass to get out too, while he, the kid, dug sand away from the spokes with his hands.

Cass gingerly stood up and stepped out on the hub of the wheel to get out. The world started spinning and he fell flat on his face in the sand. The kid came running and rolled him over so he could breathe. Cass was out cold. His eyes were rolled back and a strange wheezing noise was coming from deep down in his throat.

About nine o'clock that night a buggy came clattering through Hanksville and stopped at the Mormon Bishop's house. The boy ran to the front door and began to beat upon it with a fury. A coal oil lamp was lit and the weary-eyed bishop opened the door, still in his nightshirt.

The kid was in tears. "I got Cass Hite in the buggy and I think he's dead. We got stuck near Temple Mountain an' he fell on the ground. I think he's bad sick. Give him a blessing Bishop and make him well. His brothers'll kill me if they think I did him in."

The bishop took the lamp out to the buggy and had a look.

"Naw," he ain't dead," the bishop said. "At least not yet. Help me get him in the house."

The good bishop summoned some help, including the old woman who did most of the doctoring and midwife duties in the little community. But, other than folk medicine and home remedies, there was no real treatment to be had. The Mormons turned to their usual sure cure. Two Mormon elders anointed Cass with consecrated oil, laid their hands on his head and gave him a proper priesthood blessing, asking God to spare his life and make him well again. Cass did not regain consciousness, but he did live through the night. The Mormons took that as a sign that maybe God wasn't finished with ole Cass Hite just yet.

The next morning the bishop delivered his critically ill and still unconscious patient to the care of a widow lady in town. Mrs. Hansen had the room and the time to give her patient the full-time care he would need until he got well, or until God called him home. She had been a plural wife of one of the town's early settlers who had died a few years before.

The young man who had delivered Hite to the care of the little community asked the bishop if he would go through Cass's things and give him the money Cass had promised to pay him. Knowing that Cass would probably die, the bishop agreed. "How much does he owe you?" the bishop asked as he looked through Cass's wallet with an amazed, moon-struck look on his face.

"Five dollars," came the reply.

The bishop gave the boy a long, hard look. "Five dollars is a lot of money for a buggy ride from Green River."

"Well," the boy said, looking down at the ground. "He promised four-fifty, but I know he'd give me a fifty-cent tip for pickin' him up an' bringin' him all the way in last night."

The bishop thought about it for a moment, then handed the boy five dollars.

With a big wistful sigh and a last longing look at the wad of greenbacks in the mining man's wallet, the bishop folded the wallet and put it back in the steamer trunk. *Get thee behind me, Satan.* The good Bishop had never seen so much money in one stack. *Prospecting must pay a whole lot more than farming*, the clergyman thought.

Cass opened his eyes. With wonder he looked around the strange room. There was a woman sitting in a rocking chair near his bed. She was sleeping. He didn't recognize the woman or the room. Where was he?

Oh yes, the doctor said I've got pneumonia. Better stay in the hospital for a while.

He looked back at the sleeping woman. She was a handsome woman, wearing a high-necked modest dress with long sleeves. Her long hair was piled up on top of her head and held there with combs. A right handsome woman indeed, Cass thought. But he felt very weak and humble. Somehow, strange handsome women were not so appealing to him right then.

As he lay in the bed looking around at the unfamiliar room, the woman woke up and stared at him for a moment. Then she jumped up and hurried to his bedside.

"You're awake," she marveled. "I thought we would lose you a few days ago and now here you are, you're going to live after all."

A few days ago? What is she talking about?

"Can you eat something," the woman was saying.

Cass was still thinking about it when she came back from the kitchen.

"Here, I've got a glass of cool milk. Drink it slow. You haven't had anything on your stomach for most of a week."

The pretty woman lifted his head from the pillow and poured the milk into him. *Darn, that was good.*

Cass stayed with Mrs. Hansen for several weeks. Under her tender care he got a little stronger with each passing day. She was a good nurse. Her compassion, dedication, and fervent prayers made up for her lack of formal training.

Mrs. Hansen was an attractive, strong and healthy woman, qualities highly valued in pioneer Utah. In a larger town she would surely have had another husband by now. She had thought of leaving many times but a lack of money and courage had always held her back. Besides, Hanksville was her home. She, her sister-wives and late husband had been among the first to settle there. He had left her a comfortable little house with fruit trees and a garden.

It seemed to delight her to have someone to cook for and make a big fuss over. She had been living alone for what seemed like a long time. She was only four or five years younger than Cass and her children were mostly grown. They were all married, away at jobs, or attending school in one of the larger towns. Her late husband was living in heaven, in the fellowship of saints.

To Cass, it was wonderful to have a good woman take care of him. For the first time it made him truly understand what he had missed by remaining single all of those years. Vain and foolish women could certainly be a bother, but there was something natural and wonderful about having one around. The very sound of her voice soothed the savage soul.

At first Cass was embarrassed to be so helpless, but as he slowly began to get well he could laugh about it. Mrs. Hansen had a good sense of humor, and sometimes she teased him as she fed him with a spoon or changed his nightshirt. She smiled when she washed and groomed him, expertly trimming his moustache and cutting his hair.

As Cass began to regain his strength well enough to walk, Mrs. Hansen would have one of her former sister-wives or a young niece stay at the house during the nighttime. In a close-knit little Mormon community, even a hint of impropriety could cause a great deal of scandal.

As the first blades of tender grass began to appear along the picket fence, Cass finally felt well enough to resume his travels to Dandy Crossing. He thanked the bishop and he thanked the whole town, doing it proper and formal during a Sunday "testimony meeting" at the Mormon Church. He would certainly have died without their help, and he told them so.

It was the first and only time the old desert rat would ever attend a Mormon Church service. He felt so humbled that he almost apologized to the congregation for all of the bad things he had said about Mormons in the Denver newspapers. But he regained his self-control at the last second and pulled himself back from the brink.

Before loading his steamer trunk on the Green River Stage, bound for Hite, he opened his wallet and gave Mrs. Hansen a hundred dollars. The woman gasped and tears came to her eyes. "You don't owe me anything," she said softly, handing back the money.

"I want you to keep it," he insisted as he pressed it back into her hand.

For six weeks that good woman had nursed him, fed him, bathed him, cleaned up after him and steadied him as he re-learned to walk. A hundred dollars seemed a fair price for her troubles and saintly care.

Mrs. Hansen lowered her eyes with a wistful, almost embarrassed smile, then she put the money deep in her apron pocket. A loyal plural wife since her mid-teenage years, never in her life had she held so much money.

The stage went south to Dandy Crossing. Mrs. Hansen went back to her empty house to tidy things up now that her patient was stable. She wouldn't know for three more weeks that she was pregnant.

Cass passed through Hanksville later that year and stopped to visit with Mrs. Hansen. A different woman came to the door. She told him Mrs. Hansen had gone to live in one of the larger towns along the Wasatch Front, shortly after he had gone back to Dandy Crossing. The woman said Mrs. Hansen had married a nice widower with kids and she would soon bear a child of her own. Her letters said she was looking forward to the blessed event.

Mining Men's Pockets

For a few years the Hite brothers prospered. In the big cities, Cass and Ben Hite were seen as representatives of the golden kingdom. People had faith in them. A reasonable investment and a little luck would surely bring the treasures of the canyons. To those bold enough to dream, it would only take time and money.

But there was never enough money. The Hite brothers were building a house of cards. The gold they were finding was not enough to pay the investors. Their good name and reputation depended on paying the investors. So every few months they needed new investors to help pay the old investors. Things were getting complicated.

They tried hard to increase the yield of their mines, but flour-gold is difficult to capture. They could, and did, push more dirt through the sluice boxes, but it didn't increase the bottom line. More dirt through the sluice washed out more gold with the tailings. The gold dust needed time to settle in the rocker. Hurrying the process gained them nothing.

The only way to increase production was to hire more crews and install more machinery, thereby increasing the overhead and operational costs. It was like a cat chasing his own tail, never able to catch up, no matter how fast he ran.

Other companies along the river were having the same kinds of problems. The Glen Canyon gold rush was floating on borrowed money. Competition for investors was becoming fierce, even ruthless. The Hite brothers had to fight for their share of investment dollars.

Placer miners in Southeast Utah – 1890s
Courtesy of the Utah Historical Society

The main competition for Cass Hite turned out to be his neighbor, Adolph Kohler. Kohler's digs were near the mouth of Crescent Creek (North Wash), about five miles up the Colorado from Hite.

By 1889 there was a rough and tumble little mining camp at the mouth of Crescent Creek wearing the improbable name of Crescent City. Crescent City sported a cabin or two, a tent or two, and about a dozen gold panning residents when Robert B. Stanton stopped there during his Colorado

River railroad survey in 1889-1890. The town went downhill from there and was a complete ghost town by the turn of the century. Adolph Kohler was a prominent citizen during Crescent City's glory days. He was an executive for, The Colorado River and Utah Placer Company.

The feud began when Cass Hite, the superintendent for, The Colorado River Placer Mining Company, discovered that Kohler and his partners were selling company stock. Some people who bought the stock were confused, thinking they were investing in Cass Hite's company since the names were so similar.

To counter the confusion and potential loss of revenue, Cass put ads in several newspapers telling investors not to be deceived. Some of his ads went too far, suggesting that Kohler's stock was worth far less than Hite's. He said the Hite operation was better known, better managed, and much more productive. In fact, Cass told people he didn't think there was anything of value in the gravel bars being worked by Kohler and his partners. Had been anything worth digging there; Cass would surely have filed on it before Kohler ever came to the river.

Kohler was outraged and sought to reply in kind. Not having the same good connections the Hite brothers enjoyed in the big cities, Kohler began a smear campaign. He wrote to some of Hite's investors, making charges that raised questions about honesty and the true value of Hite's holdings along the river. He also began to put the bad mouth on Cass in places like Hanksville and Green River, trying to undermine Hite's relationship with employees, freighters and merchants.

Cass, of course, was deeply offended by the meddling in his business affairs. By the summer of 1891 the feud was reaching critical mass. There was about to be a meltdown.

The big steam engine rolled to a stop in Grand Junction, Colorado. Whistles and bells sounded loudly as steam and smoke poured out over the walkways and buildings near the depot. Passengers stepped down from the coaches to enter the buildings. The travelers were dressed in their finest apparel, wool suits and ties, long flowing dresses with fancy hats and jewelry. It was the evening of September 4, 1891. John Hite was there to meet his brother Cass.

"Well, hello Johnny, what brings you here?"

"We've gotta talk, Cass. Kohler's in Green River and he's been making threats. He's packin' a Winchester and people say he's sworn to get even. He's mad as hell about what you told those bankers in Denver."

"When did you see him last?"

"This morning. I caught the 10:30 eastbound to head you off and give you a warning. I don't know if he would really follow through with it, but I though you ought to know before you get to Green River."

"I do appreciate it, brother. Let's go over to the hotel where we can talk in private."

The two men sat in plush chairs in the hotel lobby, enjoying a stiff drink while conversing in low tones in the dim light of the oil lamps.

"Kohler's been tellin' the boys you spent the company's money on gambling and women and they won't get paid," John said. "Some of the men are nervous. You've been gone a long time."

"Are all of the men in Green River?"

"Homer and his crew are still at Dandy Crossing," John said. "The rest of them are all there, I think. Of course, they've been waitin' over two weeks, Cass. We expected you back the middle of August."

"Yeah, that damn Kohler got to me in Denver, too. That sombitch sent a letter to that Chicago syndicate sayin' our assays was all made up and there really ain't no gold on the Good Hope bar. I had to talk like a Chinaman to keep those big shots in Denver for an extra week, and they still went back to Chicago without writin' us a check. Said they'd have to consult with the board a directors before signin' anything. Good thing Kohler wasn't in Denver. I'd a dragged him out in the street and beat him to death."

"You might still get a chance," said John. "He's mad as a wet cat and he's been tellin' people he's gonna do you up right smart the first time he sees you."

"Well, we'll see about that," Cass sneered. "I guess he'll have to wait a few more days. I'm supposed ta meet a couple a men at the hotel here tomorrow to talk about some placer digs over on the Dolores."

The 6:45 westbound pulled into Green River on the evening of September 8. Cass stepped off the railcar and looked around cautiously before taking his steamer trunk from a porter. As he fished in his suit pocket for a tip, a couple of men with familiar faces came trotting over and gathered up the steamer trunk.

"Good to see ya, Cass. We was beginnin' ta think maybe ya got throwed in jail over there in Denver. Been waitin' fer ya fer darn near three weeks now. Ole Billy Bright's got a stack a I.O.U.s over at the saloon bigger'n a bale a hay. He'll sure be glad ta see you."

"Good to see you, boys," Cass smiled. "Sorry I'm so late. I got hung up with those dudes from back east there. They kept begging me to tell 'em more injun stories so it took a long time. Back East I'm beginnin' to be known as quite a Injuneer. I suspect ole Buffalo Bill will be wantin' me to be a part of his Wild West Show any time now."

"You gonna give us our pay right away, Cass?"

"I gotta get the papers together first," said Cass. "You tell the boys to come over to my cabin after breakfast in the morning and I'll settle up with everyone. See if you can round 'em all up tonight and I'll buy the drinks over at the Crescent Saloon."

"We'll sure do it, Cass, soon as we get this here trunk over to your place."

The saloon was crowded when Cass walked in and everyone stood up and gave him a big cheer. He was still in his fine suit with a starched collar and diamond stickpin. His long moustache was waxed and curled and he was wearing an expensive black hat and shiny gold cuff links. He surely looked the part of a big-time mining executive. He strode purposefully to the bar and ordered drinks for everyone. Another rowdy cheer rocked the rafters. Men crowded around, slapping him on the back, everyone trying to engage him in conversation.

It went on for half an hour before Cass noticed Adolph Kohler sitting quietly in a corner by the potbellied stove. Cass stood looking at Kohler for a moment. Kohler glared back. Cass held up the drink in his hand and said in a loud voice, "Come, have a drink, Mr. Kohler. My invitation extends to everyone."

Silence rippled through the saloon as the crowd slowly became aware of a possible armed confrontation. Men winced and looked at one another anxiously. A few began to casually move away from the two prospective combatants.

There was silence for a few moments, then Cass said again, "Come, Mr. Kohler, permit me to buy you a drink."

Kohler looked around the room suspiciously. Then he got up and walked to the opposite end of the bar from where Cass was standing. "Southern Comfort," he told the barkeeper in a strong voice. A collective sigh descended on the revelers and they all went back to the party.

Kohler looked over at Cass and held up his glass. Some might have taken it as a thank you, but both of the players knew it meant: "Sure, you bastard, I'll drink your whiskey."

The party went on without incident late into the night.

Unjustified Justifiable Homicide

The next morning about twenty men had collected at Cass Hite's cabin door before the big shot mining executive had been able to go for breakfast. In fact, he hadn't been able to wash his face or shave when they began to arrive. The men had been waiting for a long time and they were eager to collect their pay.

Cass was still hung-over drunk, but he knew the importance of keeping the men happy. He buttoned his shirt, put on his good-humored face and broke out his pay ledger and moneybox. The men were paid in cash, federal greenbacks and gold and silver coins. The double-locked moneybox had been guarded all night by two of the company's armed employees. There was no bank in Green River at the time.

Settling with the men took most of the morning. Cass retrieved a bottle of expensive whiskey from his steamer trunk and nursed his headache with alcohol as he conducted business. He had always been fond of whiskey, but lately, with all of the money he was handling on behalf of the company, he was drinking a lot. He could afford the good stuff now and he indulged himself, perhaps a little too often. The Hite brothers were having difficulty paying investors, but to attract new money they had to keep up appearances. The expense account was not something to cut.

After the workers were paid and he had a chance to clean up, Cass went to get something to eat at the Palmer House Hotel. One of his foremen, Luke Shafer, went with him. Before they left the cabin, Shafer stopped Cass and cautiously peeked out of the cabin door toward the north.

"Whatcha doin'?" Cass asked.

Kohler's stayin' at the Grammage house," said Shafer. "He's got a Winchester and he could drop you from there." The Grammage house was about a hundred yards up the street.

Shafer watched for a moment, then signaled to Cass, "Looks okay, I don't see anybody around up there."

The two men walked to the hotel and ordered lunch.

As they ate, two more of Cass's men came into the dining room. Joseph Burgess was one of them.

"You be careful, Cass," Joe said. "People say Kohler's out huntin' fer you with a rifle."

Cass dropped his fork in his plate in disgust and turned to Shafer. "I've got ta do something about this," he said.

"Whatcha gonna do?"

"I'm gonna go have a talk with that sombitch and get this thing settled." Cass said forcefully. "Will you men come with me? From what I hear, Kohler's got some men with him and I might need someone to cover my back."

The men agreed to accompany Cass to the showdown. Before they went, they walked back over to Cass Hite's cabin where they all had a good stiff drink to settle their nerves. They all checked their guns, too.

The Grammage house in Green River was not a hotel. It was a private residence with rooms to rent, a frontier boarding house with meals and an outdoor privy provided. Kohler and a couple of his men were staying there.

Mrs. Grammage, the lady who owned the place, was in her yard when she saw Cass approaching with his two companions. With anger she stepped forward to confront him. Pointing her finger back down the street, she said in a very loud voice, "Get out of here, Cass Hite, you nasty thing. You've come to cause trouble and I ain't puttin' up with it here."

Cass gently but firmly pushed her aside. His employee, Joe Burgess, took her by the arm and led her back to her kitchen, talking quietly to try to calm her down.

There was a bowery that acted as a front porch for the Grammage house. Frank Drake, Kohler's right hand man, was standing under the bowery leaning against a post. He took the toothpick from his mouth and offered Cass a chair. Cass took the chair, sat down and said, "I come to see Kohler."

"What the hell do you want?" Kohler said as he stepped from inside the house to stand in the open doorway. His face was flushed with high emotion and his Winchester was cradled over his arm, the barrel pointed toward Cass.

"Put the damn gun down and let's talk," Cass said impatiently.

Kohler lowered the rifle, then said, "Whada you got to say, you filthy lyin' bastard?"

Cass's eyes flashed with fire. He leaned forward in his chair and sneered, showing perfect contempt. "Any man who carries a Winchester looking for trouble is a cowardly son-of-a-bitch. That's what I say."

"I'll show you who's a sombitch!" Kohler jerked the rifle up and pulled the trigger.

The bullet went over Cass's head as he sat in the chair, narrowly missing Shafer who was standing slightly behind his boss. As Shafer ducked and Cass jumped to his feet, Kohler jacked another shell in the rifle and fired a second time, this time grazing Cass on his left arm.

Cass had his gun in his hand by the time he gained his feet and he shot three times from his holster in rapid succession. He missed Kohler but dropped Frank Drake who was standing between them and a little to the left. Drake was hit in the right wrist and through the right lung. It might have been the same bullet that made both wounds.

Cass turned and ran around the corner of the house as a third bullet from Kohler's rifle whistled past his head. He stopped around the corner and turned to face his opponent as Kohler came around the building in hot pursuit. Cass fired two quick shots and Kohler fired one shot, all from very close range. Then both men turned to run. Cass headed for his own cabin about a hundred yards away. Luke Shafer ran with him, his revolver drawn to cover their retreat. Joe Burgess had taken cover in the kitchen with Mrs. Grammage and missed the whole thing.

Kohler staggered and dropped his rifle in the dirt as he turned back to the bowery. He stepped over Frank Drake who was rolling around on the ground, moaning and coughing up blood. Kohler went back into the house, collapsed on the living room rug, and died. One of Cass Hite's last two bullets had drilled him, dead center.

The whole town came out on their porches and into the street at the sounds of the gunfight. People ran up and down the streets, sounding the alarm and telling the story. Cass and Shafer remained holed up in Cass's cabin, not knowing yet the results of the gunfight. Cass reloaded and had another big swig of whiskey to try to stop the shaking of his hands. The adrenaline rush was catching up with him. Burgess came running and told them Kohler was dead and Drake was mortally wounded.

The three men quickly crossed the street to the hotel where they asked the proprietor to telegraph the sheriff's office in Price to send a lawman to investigate. A couple of Kohler's men gathered up Frank Drake and carried him to the railroad depot. They put him on the next train to Salt Lake City, believing it was his only chance for survival. Green River had nothing but a funeral to offer a man with a bullet through a lung.

The county sheriff arrived the next morning accompanied by the county attorney and a justice of the peace. They held a makeshift coroner's inquest to decide guilt, justice, and the probable cause of the incident. Most of the physical evidence had been erased by then. Mrs. Grammage, being a stickler for keeping her house and yard tidy and all, had cleaned up the mess. Then too, all of the witnesses had had twenty-four hours to discuss the event and come to an agreement on what they saw and what they thought they saw.

Of course there were conflicting accounts of the incident between Cass Hite's people and Kohler's people, but it didn't take long for the coroner's jury to decide it was a case of self-defense. Justifiable homicide was the official ruling. Cass was allowed to go free and the sheriff and his people caught the next train back to Price.

That night Cass got pleasantly drunk and paid for a round of celebratory free drinks in the Crescent Saloon. While he was thus engaged, Kohler's associates were busy writing letters and keeping the telegraph lines hot with charges of a cover-up and other accusations. Cass didn't know it yet, but the fight wasn't over.

Green River, Utah – 1890s. Railroad depot and Palmer House Hotel at center.
Courtesy of Green River Archives, Green River, Utah.

Cass Hite Brought Hither

Instead of leaving Green River and going back to his mining claims at Dandy Crossing, Cass caught a train to Salt Lake City. He had more wheeling and dealing to do before going home. The newspapers reported he was in town.

The Salt Lake Tribune
September 13, 1891

Mr. Cass Hite was in the city yesterday. It will be remembered that on the 9th instant it was Mr. Hite's misfortune to be obliged to kill a stockman named A. Kohler, at Green River, Utah. The man was shooting at him with a Winchester and there was nothing to do but stop that kind of work. Mr. Hite is well known here. His family is as good as any in the world.

Mr. Hite has been on the frontier many years, and has been working a placer mine for seven or eight years down on the Colorado; and this difficulty is the first that we ever heard of his having. From what we know of him, we believe that no man need ever have trouble with him, and can fully understand why the verdict of all those who were cognizant of the shooting on the 9th instant justified his course.

Then, a month later:

The Salt Lake Tribune
October 11, 1891

Cass Hite, who recently shot two men in Green River and who was, on investigation by the Price Justice of the Peace, turned loose, is said to have been indicted by the grand jury now in session in Provo.

Kohler's friends had succeeded in getting an indictment against Cass Hite, Luke Shafer, and Joseph Burgess for the murder of Adolph Kohler and the shooting of Frank Drake. The case would be tried in the district court in Provo.

Miraculously, Frank Drake had survived both the lung shot and the long train ride to a hospital in Salt Lake without proper first aid. He was recovering well and would be the prosecution's star witness.

A warrant was issued and a federal marshal arrested Cass at his cabin in Hanksville. He was taken by train to Salt Lake for a preliminary hearing. His arrest was big news. On October 14, a headline in The Salt Lake Tribune shouted, "Cass Hite Brought Hither." The substance of the story was an interview with Cass at the marshal's office in Salt Lake.

Keys rattled as the jailer opened the big iron door of the jail cell. Cass stood up as a well-dressed man with a notebook stepped inside.

"Thank you for agreeing to speak with me, Mr. Hite."

Turning on his charm and his best formal language, Cass said, "My pleasure, Mr. Armstrong. Please sit down, sir. I'm sorry the corner of the bunk is all I can offer you. Only the jailer rates a chair in this establishment."

"No problem, Mr. Hite. I've been here before." Then, getting right to business, the reporter asked, "What do you have to say about your arrest, sir?"

"I'm not surprised by my arrest," said Cass. "I've been expecting it. Although it is not in the least pleasant, I have nothing to fear so far as the final outcome is concerned. The shooting, of course, will be a source of life-long regret to me, but I could not, under the circumstances, have done other than I did."

"Will you endeavor to have an immediate trial?" the reporter asked.

"No, for my witnesses are scattered all over the country and it will take at least six weeks before I am ready."

"Who are acting as prosecutors?"

"Well, of course I have enemies, most businessmen do. But I understand that a fellow named Mansfield, who has more money than brains, has sent 500 dollars with which to prosecute me. But it will do him no good. The coroner's jury exonerated me, and Mr. Ullanger, the prosecuting attorney for Emery County, refused to hold a preliminary examination because he believed I was justified."

"Are you in a position to give bail, sir?"

"Yes, there will be no trouble about bail. I can give a bond in almost any amount. I have letters and telegrams from friends all over the country offering to be my surrogates."

"What were the circumstances of your conflict with Mr. Kohler?"

"The evidence will show that I was attacked and my opponent fired first," said Cass. "Other than that, I must decline further comment at this time. My attorney has advised me to save my testimony for presentation before the court. I will say that I have many friends in this city willing to testify of my good character and peaceful disposition. This incident is most unfortunate, and I do hope people will reserve their judgment until I have had my time in court."

"Any further comments, Mr. Hite?"

"None at this time."

"Thank you, sir."

Cass was outraged that the trial would be held in Provo. Utah's second largest city was a long way from Green River and he wouldn't have a jury of his peers there. In his mind, he had no peers there. His peers were rough and tumble mining men who understood gunfights and self-defense. Provo was the heart of Zion, the very epicenter of Mormonism. What would Latter-Day-Saints know about a man's honor and his right to settle a score?

Cass had tried to turn a page and reconcile his differences with Mormons after his convalescent stay with Mrs. Hansen. His heartfelt thank you to the little town of Hanksville had been sincere. But now, as the realization settled that Provo Mormons would be his judge and jury, his old fears and prejudices came roaring back. A jury of Provoites would surely be contaminated with priesthood brethren. Hell, there might even be an undercover Avenging Angel or two on the jury.

It was too late for Cass to repent of the hateful things he had said about Mormons in the Colorado newspapers, so he immediately set out to secure the best legal counsel a high-class, non-Mormon mining executive could buy.

A bail hearing was held in Provo on December 14. Assistant U.S. attorney J.M. Zane represented the good people of Utah Territory. An attorney the newspapers called Judge Powers, represented Cass Hite. Cass's brother, Luke Hite, assisted Judge Powers. Luke was an attorney from Missouri who had come west to help his younger brother in his hour of need. After hearing testimony from several witnesses, district Judge Blackburn set Hite's bail at $20,000 – a high mark to reach, even for a big-time mining executive.

Provo's newspaper, The Daily Enquirer, said Cass was visibly affected at the end of the hearing when friends crowded around him to shake hands and offer words of encouragement. He did have a lot of friends, and many pledged their property and bank accounts to help secure his temporary freedom pending trial.

Liars, Lawyers, and a Lack of Luck

The murder trial began on February 26, 1892. The prosecution laid out their case, stating that Cass, Shafer, and Burgess, had gone to the Grammage house to pick a fight and Kohler had been killed with premeditation.

Cass Hite's new lawyer, Mr. Hiles, said in his opening statements he would prove that Kohler had conspired to kill Cass when Cass came back from Denver, and the shooting was a matter of self-defense. He said the trouble started when Cass had exposed the worthlessness of Kohler's mining claims and Kohler took offense. He said Kohler had shown premeditation when he had his will drawn up shortly before Cass came back to Green River, proving that he expected to be involved in a deadly fight.

The attorney said Cass had only two choices that day in Green River. He could leave town, or he could go to Kohler and try to settle things. He said Cass Hite was "as brave as he was humane, and not the kind of man to submit to being run out of town." The attorney said Luke Shafer and Joseph Burgess had no more to do with the killing than did the jury. The only reason they were indicted was to discredit their testimony on Cass Hite's behalf.

Over the next week, several witnesses were examined. Kohler's men testified to the murder of their innocent boss. Cass Hite's men testified that Kohler had shot twice before Cass could draw his gun. Mrs. Grammage testified of Cass Hite's bad character. The defense brought several people to testify of his good character. Details of the shooting were examined and reexamined several times by many alleged eyewitnesses and after-the-fact participants.

Frank Drake took the stand and said he was unarmed when shot by Cass Hite. He also testified that Kohler didn't own a gun, but had borrowed the rifle from Mr. Brown of Green River when he learned there might be trouble. He said Hite had insulted Kohler, and when Kohler insulted him back, Hite had yelled, "take it back," and drew his gun and fired. Kohler then picked up his rifle and shot back in self-defense. He said Hite had shot him (Drake) while Cass and Shafer were running away, after shooting Kohler.

Cass Hite took the stand and said he didn't know that Frank Drake had been hit until after the gunfight. He said it was an accident and Drake knew it was so. He said Drake had told people that Cass wasn't at fault – he (Drake) just got in the way.

Cass testified that he had bought Kohler and Drake drinks at the Crescent Saloon the night before the shooting, and that showed that he harbored no bad feelings. He said he had gone to the Grammage house only to talk, but Kohler was acting crazy and didn't make sense. Kohler fired first and Cass only did what he had to do to protect himself.

Cass said he didn't take his gun to the Grammage house to shoot Kohler. He just happened to have it with him when the trouble started. It was his custom to carry firearms since he lived at Dandy Crossing and it was a dangerous place, frequented by outlaws and Indians.

On cross examination by the prosecuting attorney, Cass said yes, reports Kohler sent to Denver had prevented him from getting money he needed to pay his men. And yes, he did have bad feelings about that when he returned to Green River. He was angry about the stories Kohler had been telling his employees and other people in town, too.

Zane then asked if Cass and Billy Bright, who was said to be a master engraver, had ever conspired to counterfeit twenty-dollar gold pieces and circulate them in Mexico. Cass said it wasn't true.

Closing arguments were made on March 4 and the jury retired to deliberate. Unfortunately, they were unable to decide. The jury returned to the courthouse hopelessly deadlocked, two in favor of acquittal, ten voting to convict. The judge declared a mistrial and bound the case over to be tried again. The one bright note was that Luke Shafer and Joe Burgess were both declared not guilty of all charges.

Cass was again able to gain temporary freedom though the $20,000 bond. When released on bail he went back to Colorado to try to raise more money for his defense and his troubled mining empire. Even with his life and liberty resting on the scales of justice, along the Colorado, the show must go on. Business can't wait for a courtroom verdict.

Before the second trial, Cass petitioned for a change of venue. He was convinced that the prejudices of the Mormons were the cause of the hung jury. Had he faced a jury of hardy outdoorsmen, he would surely have won an acquittal. He wanted to take his case back to Emery County, to Price, Castle Dale, or Green River. To his dismay and disgust, his petition was denied.

The second trial was again held in Provo. Testimony began on October 5, 1892. Mr. Hiles, who had represented Cass at the first trial, was still a member of the defense team, but there was a new face, too. Cass had secured the services of a high-class, top-drawer attorney from Denver known as Colonel Montgomery.

The Colonel brought a whole new feel to the court proceedings. He was arrogant and disrespectful, giving the impression that working his magic in the lowly federal court in Provo, Utah, was somehow beneath him.

Basically, the trial followed the same pattern as the first trial. The same witnesses were called, the same testimony given, the same points debated between the prosecution and defense. One difference was that Colonel Montgomery was able to discredit the testimony of a couple of Kohler's witnesses.

Closing arguments began on October 11. A Provo newspaper summed it all up beautifully, inserting a little wit and humor in the report.

The Daily Herald
October 12, 1892

Colonel Montgomery devoted considerable time towards the prosecuting attorney [Mr. Zane] referring to him as a young man wearing a size 6 hat and size 11 shoes, the latter generally red [sissified]. Judge Blackburn several times called the Colorado attorney to order, whereupon he remarked that he had practiced law so long that he could adapt himself to almost any court.

His plea was powerful and interspersed with chilling snows of sarcasm, which fell upon the heads of the prosecuting attorney and prosecuting witnesses.

He appealed to reason and the strong Western manhood of the jurors, rather than to their tender feelings. There was a tremor of tenderness, however, in his tone in his concluding remarks when he referred to his friendship with Cass Hite. Hite was affected by the remarks and applied his kerchief to his eyes.

The Salt Lake Tribune completed the story the following day:

The Salt Lake Tribune
October 13, 1892

Mr. Zane made the closing argument for the prosecution. In a sarcastic and good-natured manner, he referred to the abuse that had been heaped upon him by Colonel Montgomery.

The criticism made upon Mr. Zane's youth, personal appearance and conduct in the case by Colonel Montgomery yesterday were returned with interest, and the conduct of the Colonel claimed to be unprofessional, earnestly renounced and ridiculed. Judge Blackburn finally called Zane to order as he did Colonel Montgomery on Tuesday.

A very interesting and impressive incident happened at the close of Mr. Zane's arguments. A delegation of three ladies came to the courthouse bearing a magnificent bouquet, to which was attached a card bearing on one side the inscription, "Compliments of the ladies of Provo to Cass Hite: October 12, 1892" on the other side was written: "God is our refuge and strength, a very present help in time of trouble – Psalms 46.1"

As the jury filed out to deliberate, Cass stood beaming with a magnificent bouquet on one arm and a pretty girl on the other. Colonel Montgomery had got the last word. It was a final appeal to, "the strong Western manhood of the jurors."

Young women bearing flowers was an incredibly bold piece of legal burlesque for a conservative town like Provo. It was a good try, but the gentile colonel had misread his Mormon jury. The stunt apparently backfired.

The jury didn't take long. They were sent to deliberate about 4 p.m. and brought in a verdict at 10:10 the following morning, after enjoying a good breakfast. The court was hushed as Mr. George Mcklusky, the jury foreman, pronounced: "We the jury find the defendant, Cass Hite, guilty of murder in the second degree with recommendation of mercy from the court."

Judge Blackburn dropped his gavel, sentencing Cass to 12 years in the Territorial Prison.

Cass Hite and Colonel Montgomery couldn't believe it. They asked to have the jury polled. They asked to have the verdict thrown out in favor of a new trial. They asked for a stay of execution of the sentence to allow time for an appeal, and they asked to have Cass freed on bail until the appeal was ruled on.

Judge Blackburn agreed only to a delay in imposing the sentence to allow for appeal. He ordered Cass to be locked up in the Provo City Jail pending the outcome.

Keep the Home Fires Burning

Though Cass had many friends and was generally well respected, the Hite brothers' mining empire began to crumble after he was arrested for murder. The bad publicity cast a shadow over everything. To some, his conviction for murder verified the things Adolph Kohler had been saying about his character.

The problem wasn't just Cass Hite's credibility. The Glen Canyon gold rush was losing its sparkle. Men of means had been sinking money in the canyons for five or six years and most had little to show for their investment. The word was getting out.

At Dandy Crossing things were tight. Cass's legal bills were draining the company coffers. Employees had to be paid, and Colonel Ben's nonstop investor-hunting expeditions were expensive. Long-time investors were demanding their promised returns and Colonel Ben was finding it ever more difficult to attract new investors.

But then, just when they needed it most, a ray of sunshine broke through the dark clouds of gloom. There was a renewed interest in placer mining along the San Juan River during the winter of 1892-93. Some called it the San Juan River gold rush.

Colonel Ben rejoiced. The possibility of another mining boom, anywhere in the area, might prove to be a lifeboat. With scores of starry-eyed new gold seekers passing through the area, they might be able to sell or lease a few more mining claims. Then too, they owned the only store for almost a hundred miles in any direction. Shoot, they might even make a little money ferrying prospectors across the river. It was time to actively promote, "Dandy Crossing."

On January 13, 1893 The Ogden Standard Examiner ran a story with the headline: "Gold Excitement Continues – Notwithstanding the Diverse Reports."

Ben Hite was the principal source of the story, trying valiantly to convince hardy gold seekers that pay dirt on the Colorado sparkled brighter than the sands of San Juan.

> Several prominent Salt Lake capitalists are heavily interested in the Colorado River as well as the San Juan River placers, out of which much pay dirt has already been taken. Colonel Ben Hite of Dandy Crossing, who controls the Good Hope and Ticaboo bars said, "We regard the placers on the Colorado River in Utah as being very valuable and would have

taken out a great deal of gold were we not unfortunate with our machinery. We shall renew operations at once on an enlarged scale. Our dirt runs from $2.50 upward per yard. Parties with small appliances are taking out from $6 to $10 per day each man. Their claims are just below us toward the San Juan."

Colonel Ben was desperate. He was fudging the numbers. That same year, Cy Warman, a reliable source, estimated the average yield of the Colorado River placers at 20 to 60 cents per yard. Even at $2.50 per yard, there is no way a man with a gold pan could wash enough dirt to make 6 or 10 dollars a day.

Ben went on to say, "Yes, the Henry Mountains are full of minerals. I consider the Bromine Mine [Eagle City] sold very cheap at $40,000. Very little of the Henry Mountains have been prospected [a shameful lie] and when it is more thoroughly worked I believe great developments in rich gold ore will be shown. A pronounced rush may be expected in the spring."

Then, drawing attention to Dandy Crossing, Ben said the best, shortest, and safest route to the San Juan gold fields was the Green River stage to Dandy Crossing. The Dandy Crossing ferry is now in operation, he said, and a prospector could reach the San Juan River in a day and a half up the White Canyon road. The entire route, he said, was "all that could be desired."

A similar article ran in the Aspen Weekly Times on January 21, 1893. Colonel Ben was making the newspaper circuit, indulging in shameless self-promotion. He was a true pioneer in capitalist propaganda. Not content to simply promote Dandy Crossing as the best road to the San Juan, he was now using fear of the Indians as an inducement.

Mr. Hite says that while there has not been any serious trouble as yet with the Indians, it might break out at any moment. The disposition of the prospectors is to overflow - to expand - and if they enter the reservation there will be trouble.

The presence of so many men flocking in from Flagstaff and Winslow and via Durango and Dolores has had an irritating effect on the Navajos, and while they would not bother any outside the reservation, they are not inclined to look favorably on the presence of so many men passing through or skirting along the country.

For this reason he said the trip via Green River is much to be preferred. It is not necessary to go through the reservation, as the route from that point to Dandy Crossing is straight south and some distance away from the Navajo country. The road is not only shorter, but over better roads and through settlements.

Ben also tried to give prospectors a reason to stay on the Colorado. "There is no doubt about the existence of fine gold on the San Juan," he said, "but it is not to be compared to the coarse and larger deposits found on the Colorado River." [Large deposits of coarse gold on the Colorado River? Surely Ben knew better.] "I am still a firm believer in the Colorado River country. It will yet be found that this country below Dandy Crossing and the lode mining in the Henry Mountains is infinitely richer than the San Juan. It is no longer a mere suspicion – it is a well-developed fact."

Cass Hite, too, wrote a long letter to the newspapers from the Provo City Jail. Like his brother Ben, he was trying to promote Dandy Crossing. His letter is dated January 1, 1893, and was originally sent to the Denver Republican. The Salt Lake Tribune carried the story on January 12, 1893.

The Tribune introduction to his letter reads in part: "Everyone who has heard of the Colorado and San Juan where the gold fever is currently, has heard of Cass Hite. No man has explored the area more than he has. His name has been a part of that country since he first went there. With his ten years of explorations, there is no one better qualified to write a description of the country."

In his letter, Cass gives a long and detailed description of the canyon country, his views on the mineral prospects of the region and a few details of his early explorations. Predictably, like his brother Ben, his assessment of the gold mining potential of the San Juan turned into a promotion of his holdings on the Colorado.

"I never found anything there [the San Juan] that a poor man could work, although I am convinced I know of much good gold property in that section that could be worked at a good profit with capital enough to put it in working order.

"That is a good gold country, and the fact that I did not strike it rich in there is no reason in the world why others may not. I drifted over to the Colorado and found Dandy Crossing, Ticaboo and Good Hope, where I could, and did, live for years with a rocker [sluice box]. I believe that the beds of those streams [Colorado River tributaries] are yellow. The gold on those streams will last for a century of active mining."

A beautifully detailed, hand drawn map of Southeast Utah was included and published with the letter (see page 5).

Enoch Davis and the Lost Rhodes Mine

While Cass Hite languished in the Provo City jail, writing letters and dreaming of happier times, Colonel Montgomery's appeals went all the way to the Territorial Supreme Court. Unfortunately, the judgment went against him. On April 17, 1893, Cass was remanded to the custody of federal marshals to begin serving his twelve-year sentence in the territorial prison.

Cass was placed in a cell with another convicted murderer. The man was Enoch Davis and he had killed his wife. Davis was from Vernal and he had a date with a firing squad. He paced the cell like a caged cat, bemoaning his fate and cursing the gods of ill fortune.

Davis beat his wife to death, he said, when he caught her in his bed with the town doctor. Doctors made house calls in those days. He would have cured the doctor's ills, but his gun jammed. Deprived of righteous justice by a malfunctioning firearm, the amorous medical practitioner fled to Salt Lake City where he thoughtfully committed suicide.

The only reason Davis was convicted, he said, was because he failed to notify the authorities right away. He didn't mention that he threw his wife's body in a potato pit and covered her up, swearing his four children to silence. The kids didn't take the oath seriously and told Grandma all about it.

The cell was small and the men had no one else to talk to. Cass didn't like this pathetic fellow much, but he was the only companion to his misery. They traded life stories and talked of happier times. Cass was sick a lot and Enoch Davis helped to nurse him along. Cass was 48 years old and suffering from alcohol withdrawal, a chronic lung ailment, and perhaps the early onset of heart disease.

Davis was understandably anxious and he talked a lot, trying to justify himself in the eyes of his cellmate. With the day of his execution set, he brooded about the meaning of life and his future in heaven or hell.

The two men were sitting idly in their cell one day. Cass was reading a newspaper while Davis sat staring at the floor, his mind off in other climes, in other times and other places. Finally, he spoke.

"I've been sentenced to be shot, you know."

"That's what I heard," Cass said from behind his newspaper.

"Wonder what it's like to be shot. Have you ever been shot, Cass?"

"No, I've never been shot."

"But you have shot others. That's why you're in here."

Cass remained impatiently silent.

"I wonder if everything just goes black, or if there really is a great beyond filled with angels and rainbows and streets paved with gold and all."

Cass didn't say anything.

"Tell me, Cass," Davis insisted. "What do you think? Is there another world after this one, or what?

"The only world I know about is this one," Cass said, looking over the newspaper.

"But them preachers and Mormons all say there's another world beyond this one," Enoch argued. "They say all we gotta do is follow the good shepherd Jesus and we'll all be saved and live happily ever after in that big kingdom in the sky."

Cass put down his newspaper.

"You be careful, Davis. I ain't ever gonna say anything disrespectful about Jesus. I just don't know about all of that religion stuff."

"You've never been a member of the flock?"

"I've been to church, but I've never been a sheep," Cass said. "I have been around a few preachers, those good shepherds who look after the flock, and I can tell you that most of 'em make their living the same as regular sheepherders. They fleece the flock."

Davis laughed.

"But I can tell you, Davis, there is something out there beyond what we normally see and hear. I found that out when I was livin' amongst them Indians. That old chief Hoskininni has some miraculous powers. He's a medicine man as well as a chief, and I saw some things I can't explain. That old Injun could cure people, sure enough. He would paint pictures in the dirt using colored sand, and then he'd sing and work himself into a trance. He had a ragged old buffalo tail he'd wave over the sick person and he'd moan and groan and growl like a wild cat and that sick person would sure as hell get better.

"He could see things a hundred miles away, too. He'd go into that trance and lay there by the fire like he was dead, and when he'd wake up, he'd tell things that were goin' on clear across the territory. I found out later the things he told were true. He could look into the fire and tell his hunters where to go to find deer, too.

"So, I don't know about angels and heaven and streets paved with gold, but I can tell you true, there's somethin' strange out there we don't know about."

In the course of trading stories, Cass told Davis all about his quest for the lost silver mine of the Navajos and his efforts to recover gold from the Colorado River sands. Davis was intrigued, and one day he made a confession to Cass Hite. He said he had known the Rhoades family as a child, and he was the only man alive who knew the location of the Lost Rhoades Mine in the Uintah Mountains.

At first Cass thought the man was a shameless liar. But the more Davis talked, the more intriguing the tale became. Soon, Cass was asking a lot of questions and mentally taking notes. It was a wild and improbable tale the wife killer was telling, but there was a hopeful ring of truth about it, too. The story was rooted in Mormon folklore and the Mormons did seem to have an uncanny ability to find gold when they needed it. It was Mormons, after all, who found the first gold in California, just in time to help their struggling new settlements in the Great Basin.

Everyone in Utah knew stories of Mormon gold. The Mormon prophet, Joseph Smith, had found gold plates with ancient writing buried near Palmyra, New York. And once they got to Utah, some Mormons said Brigham Young had a secret, holy gold mine in the mountains guarded by Indians. Mormons were the only people ever to find silver in sandstone at Silver Reef in southwest Utah. There was even a dream mine. A visionary Mormon bishop had been visited by an angel in a dream and shown a dike of pure gold in the Timpanogos Mountains. He and faithful members of his congregation were sinking a shaft to locate it. The angel said the gold would save the church and the nation from future bankruptcy.

Most practical, non-Mormon men like Cass dismissed stories of heavenly revealed gold as religious nonsense. But now, in the confines of their tiny prison cell, Enoch Davis was making a believer out of Cass Hite. Cass asked him to relate the full story of the Lost Rhoades Mine as told by the Mormon faithful.

Enoch, the condemned, complied:

Shortly after settling in the Salt Lake Valley, Brigham Young baptized a Ute Indian chief named Walkara, whom the Mormons called Chief Walker. Brother Brigham and the Indian became good friends.

Walkara invited the Mormons to settle on "his" land, known as the Sanpete Valley. In the course of their discussions, the Indian told Brigham about a fabulously rich gold mine in the mountains east of Salt Lake that the Indians kept hidden. Early Spaniards had developed the mine, but they were not good neighbors and the Utes had plowed them under.

Promising to be a good neighbor, Brigham Young cut a deal with Walkara to allow one trusted Mormon Elder to go there to recover the gold to help build up the Kingdom of God in the Salt Lake Valley. The man selected for the mission was Thomas Rhoades.

Thomas (the giant – said to be almost seven feet tall) Rhoades, was an early convert to Mormonism who migrated to California in 1846, a full year before Brigham Young led the saints to the Salt Lake Valley. Thomas was at Sutter's Mill with members of the Mormon Battalion when gold was discovered there in 1848. The next year he traveled east to the newly established Salt Lake City.

In Salt Lake, the giant gave Brigham Young a tithe and an offering totaling $17,000 in gold, a fortune at the time. He deposited another $11,000 in gold in a personal account at the Deseret Mint, owned and operated by the church. Brigham Young appointed him treasurer of the mint since he was the largest single depositor. Thomas was chosen by Brigham Young to go to the secret mine because he had already shown his faithfulness by giving the church a fortune in gold.

Thomas, and later his son, Caleb, made several trips into the Uintah Mountains and returned with saddlebags filled with gold. The Rhoades men, father and son, were sworn by priesthood oath to go there only for the church and never keep any of the treasure for themselves.

True to the oath they had taken, the men never revealed the source of the gold or the location of the mine. They faithfully gave the gold to brother Brigham who had it cast into coins. The coins were the official currency of the State of Deseret, as the Mormons first called their new home in the mountains. The gold pieces, in various denominations, had the clasped hands of fellowship on one side and "Holiness to the Lord," on the other. The church mint made the coins from 1849 to 1860.

By the time the transcontinental railroad was completed in 1869, the saints were back to using regular American money again. With no further need for the Spanish gold, Brigham Young relieved the Rhoades men of their mission and instructed them never to go back to the mine. They didn't.

For generations the tale of the Lost Rhoades Mine was whispered in the Mormon communities. Eventually, no one could be sure if the story was a memory, or a myth.

Enoch Davis told Cass that a son of Thomas Rhoades had been his playmate when they were boys. He had spent considerable time in the Rhoades home and once saw a large wooden bowl filled with glittering gold nuggets the old giant had brought back from the mountains. .

Davis said he met his old playmate, Enoch Rhoads, at Fort Duchesne many years after their childhood frolics. The son of the giant told Davis he was on his way to find his father's gold. The old man had drawn a map to the secret mine just before he died. He invited Davis to accompany him, seeing as how they had been such good childhood friends and all.

Davis said he and Enoch Rhoades went into the mountains in 1885 and found the lost mine. Unfortunately, the Indians discovered them there and Enoch Rhoades was killed. Davis got away with just one small rock in his pocket containing flecks of gold. He didn't dare go back to the mine alone, and he couldn't take other men back to bury his old friend without disclosing the location of the treasure. So he simply returned to Fort Duchesne and resumed his life as a blacksmith, never telling anyone of his adventure. The bones of his dear friend were scattered by coyotes and other vermin.

For eight years Davis had kept his secret, planning to recover the treasure when conditions were more favorable, but alas, it never happened. Now, here he was, convicted of killing that trollop of a wife, awaiting the executioner while dreaming of all that unclaimed gold over on the Uintahs.

"Why didn't you go back to that mine?" Cass asked incredulously.

"It's on the reservation," Enoch Davis said. "Wouldn't do no good to try to claim it if it's on Indian ground. The government wouldn't allow it and the Indians would kill me if they caught me snoopin' around up there. I was gonna wait 'til they open the reservation for white settlement. Then I'd go in there and stake a claim or homestead the site. Besides, some say there's a curse on that gold. No white man is supposed ta touch it lest he takes that priesthood oath."

"Look here, Davis. There's a petition goin' around askin' the governor to pardon me. I've got a lot a friends, here in Utah and all over these United States. My lawyer is workin' things out. He says there's a good chance I might be out a here in a few months. Why, I could go find that gold and we could use it to buy your freedom."

"I've been sentenced to be shot."

"Yes, I know, but money can buy anything. When the governor and legislature see all the wealth you'll be bringing to the territory, and the people see all the good things it will do, you'll surely be able to get a second trial, or at least a commutation of your death sentence. You might even get a full pardon, who knows? I'm tellin' ya Davis, it's worth a shot."

With nothing to lose and everything to gain, Davis made Cass a map on condition that he use the gold to get Davis released from prison. They would then split what was left. Cass agreed. The Lost Rhoades Mine would surely be worth millions.

On October 29, 1893, the arrogant and expensive Denver lawyer, Colonel Montgomery, came through in spades. Cass received a full pardon from the territorial governor.

The Colonel had conducted a massive petition drive to have Cass released. Copies of the petition had been circulated throughout Utah Territory and across the country in places like Colorado, Texas, and Missouri, where Cass had friends and family.

In granting the pardon, Governor West said he had been convinced that Cass was "not of the criminal class, but from a respectable, law-abiding family and well brought up." The killing of Kohler, he said, "was one of those unfortunate occurrences in which any peaceable and well-disposed citizen might have become involved." His decision was influenced, "by many thoughtful and considerate men, including eight of the jurors who convicted the prisoner, who ask for his release for good and sufficient reasons."

Colonel Montgomery had earned his hefty fee. After eighteen months of litigation that included two trials, a murder conviction, appeals all the way to the Territorial Supreme Court and a well coordinated petition drive; Cass walked out of prison a free man. He had spent eight months and five days in the Provo City Jail, and six months and twelve days in the penitentiary.

Cass was nearly broke when he left the prison, both his money and his health, but he had a map to the Lost Rhoades Mine. He couldn't have asked for a better going home present. The prospects of a new adventure boosted his spirits and recharged his dwindling reserves of energy and health. Wagon loads of gold or not, the map itself was a sure ticket to the bank accounts of some wealthy investors.

To regain his professional facade, Cass rented a room in the best hotel in Salt Lake, bought a bottle of good whiskey, and began poring over maps of the Uintah Mountains. His brothers would have to take care of things along the Colorado for a while.

Expedition to the Uintahs

Within days of getting out of prison, Cass was making contacts with rich and powerful men in Salt Lake City. He would have preferred to keep his mission secret while searching for the mine himself, but he didn't have the funds. The Uintahs were rough, wild, and for the most part, unexplored. Indians claimed most of the area by treaty and Cass had never been there. A successful prospecting expedition would take a large, well-armed and well-equipped party. Cass put on his most confident face, adjusted his attitude and polished his language.

The well-dressed man behind the mahogany desk smiled and extended his hand.

"How are you, Mr. Hite? My secretary said you had something to tell me that could only be discussed in private."

"That is true," said Cass as he pulled a well-stuffed chair up closer to the desk. "I want to give you first chance to get in on this deal."

"Ah, another deal it is," the rich man smiled. He paused to lift a flask of whiskey and a couple of small glasses from inside his desk. "How is my property along the Colorado doing?"

"As you know, Mr. Rognon, I have been somewhat indisposed this past year or two. However, my brother, Colonel Ben, tells me we should do much better once the new machinery is in full operation. There's a fortune in gold there, to be sure. You have seen the samples and the assays."

"Yes, I have," the rich man said with a just a touch of sarcasm.

Cass didn't respond.

"So, Mr. Hite, what is this new prospect all about?"

"I have information about a gold hoard on the Uintah Mountains."

"Do tell," the rich man smiled, lifting his glass in salutation.

"As you know," Cass began. "I have recently been favored to abide in state sponsored accommodations. While there, I was most fortunate to meet a fellow who grew up in the household of the giant Rhoades, the man whom the late prophet Brigham Young would send into the mountains to bring back gold for the Mormon Church. Perhaps you are familiar with the stories?"

"Yes," the rich man nodded. "I am familiar with the stories."

"Well," Cass continued. "My informant tells me that none other than the son of the old giant took him to the site and he did behold the wonders. He says it is a cave, or a mine, deep in the mountains that literally shines in the light of a torch with pure gold."

"And?" the rich man questioned as he poured each of them another drink.

"My informant is sentenced to die," Cass explained. "He will not be going back to the treasure. After some weeks, I was able to persuade him to draw me a map with directions to the site. I have the map in my pocket. But of course, I will not be able to show it to you until we have signed an agreement. I'm sure you understand."

The rich man smiled.

"How much do you need," he asked.

"It will require a full expedition into the mountains," Cass began. "I will need a full complement of supplies and hired men for security. I am told the Indians are bad out that way. I will need horses and ..."

"How much do you need," the rich man interrupted, somewhat impatiently.

"Six hundred dollars," Cass said flatly.

"Good hell, man, you're not going to Africa. I can perhaps give you four hundred, for a full fifty-percent share."

"I have calculated the expenses and four hundred will not do," Cass insisted. "I'm going into unfamiliar territory and I might be there for many weeks."

The rich man remained silent, refusing to make the next move.

"Tell you what," Cass said after an awkward pause. "Four hundred will buy a thirty-percent share. I'll have to find other investors to make up the difference. I'm sure you understand."

"I'll give you four hundred dollars for a 50-percent share in the lost mine and any other plunder or mining prospects you might find," the man said. "That's the best I can do."

Cass thought it over for a moment or two.

"Give me four hundred and pay my bill over at the hotel," Cass said with an embarrassed smile.

"And how much is your bill over at the hotel," the rich man asked with an air of amusement.

"A little over forty dollars last time I checked," Cass winced, looking down at the floor. "I have a small line of credit at the bar, as well. You've got to understand. I've been out of circulation for a time and those big city lawyers got most of my money."

"Four hundred dollars and I'll pay your hotel and bar tab," the rich man offered. "But I want 50-percent of anything that comes from this expedition of yours."

"Make that 45-percent," Cass argued. "I do have other options."

"Forty-eight percent. Take it or leave it," the rich man said, wearing his best poker playing face.

"We can do that," Cass agreed.

"Good, I'll have my secretary draw up the papers. And, I want to see that map and have my man make a copy, right here and now. How soon will you be ready to go?"

"There's still ten feet of snow on those mountains," said Cass with some alarm. "Besides, it'll take some time to round up all the gear and hire the men I need."

"Here's my check for four hundred dollars," the rich man said. "I'll have my man stop at the hotel and settle your account this afternoon. Spend your money wisely, Mr. Hite. From here on out your room and bar tab are up to you."

The month of May would have been the best time to go, but the Hite expedition headed into the mountains in mid-February 1894. They crept out of town in the dead of night, hoping not to be noticed. Cass was angry. There was still snow in the mountains and it was way too early in the season for prospecting, but they had to hurry since word had leaked out and other parties were planning to dog their trail. Salt Lake was abuzz with stories that Cass Hite was on the trail to Brigham Young's secret mine in the mountains. Some men even claimed to have copies of Hite's secret map and were planning to race him to the spot.

Hite's midnight departure signaled the start of the Uintah Mountain gold rush. It was a gold rush like no other. No pay dirt had been found, no nuggets produced, no assays reported. The whole thing was based on folklore, rumor, religious gossip, and the word of a convicted murderer.

The prospecting party traveled to Vernal, and shortly thereafter struck out for the mountains in the mud and snow. The going was rough and camping was tough. They made a base camp in the foothills where the snow had melted back enough to present a few dry spots to pitch tents. From there they plowed their horses into the snowdrifts, attempting to follow the Enoch Davis map.

Cass soon discovered that the map and the topography didn't line up very well. What should have been an easy route to the lost mine turned out to be a maze of tangled canyons, steep slopes and heavy timber. None of those things showed up on the flat piece of paper Enoch Davis had drawn his map on.

There were other problems, too. As the weather warmed, more and more hopeful prospectors showed up on the fringes of their camps. There were shadows of men back in the trees, like hungry wolves, watching, waiting, and trying to guess where Cass and his team would search next. The anxious, greedy spectators were a worrisome bunch, but most stayed back and out of the way. Cass Hite's reputation as a gunman and convicted murderer served him well. Most prospective claim jumpers gave him a wide berth.

The search continued as the snow slowly melted and the calendar was turned to April, then May, and finally June.

It was late afternoon when riders came up the valley with a long string of packhorses following the crooked trail like a huge slithering snake. It was the supply detail returning from Vernal. The man in the lead shouted as he trotted his horse into the camp, "Where's Hite. I got news for Cass Hite."

Cass stepped out of his tent, pulling on his jacket against the cold mountain air.

"Someone found it, Cass," the horseman shouted from the saddle as he came closer. "It's all over the papers. Some dude found that Lost Rhoades Mine."

"What are you talking about?" Cass growled as he stepped forward.

The horseman pulled his mount to a stop, almost running over Cass who had to step back to keep from being trampled. "Read it and weep," the man said as he tossed down a rolled-up newspaper tied with a string.

Cass caught the newspaper in the air and quickly unrolled it. The front page screamed at him: Vernal Express, June 14, 1894 - Found at Last - The Fabulously Rich Enoch Davis Gold Mine by Dallin and Hatch.

Cass was incensed. With angry eyes he read the story aloud as members of his team stood around with bowed heads and worried expressions.

The story said George Dallin, a prospector from Salt Lake, and Lorenzo Hatch, a prominent citizen of Vernal, had found the mine and staked a claim. The story said Lorenzo Hatch had a brother who had been a partner with Enoch Davis in discovering the mine back in '85. When Lorenzo heard that Cass was on his way to find the mine, he enlisted the services of prospector George Dallin and beat Cass there. There was no mention why Lorenzo Hatch's brother hadn't gone back to the mine himself.

Enoch Davis said the mine was on the reservation, but the two men who found it were convinced that it lay outside the boundary. If true, their claim gave them legal title. The newspaper said the mineral vein was 15 feet thick and the assay office expected the ore would run about 300 dollars per ton, a very rich find.

The news was a heavy blow to Cass. His reputation was damaged. After all of the newspaper publicity, people would surely be laughing. But, while the newspaper called it a sure thing, Cass was not so sure. The area where the men found their gold was not on the Enoch Davis map. He couldn't believe Davis could have been so wrong. Surely, the lost mine was still out there somewhere. He wasn't about to give up his dream because some newspaper got the story wrong.

The problem he faced now was credibility. His wealthy partner might revolt after hearing the news. In May Cass had traveled back to Salt Lake to give Mr. Rognon a report and ask for more money. Cass had convinced the moneyman to continue grubstaking his efforts after the original $400 had run out. If he kept looking for the real mine, he would still need to eat. He couldn't let his grubstake dry up.

To redeem himself in the eyes of the world and his wealthy benefactor, Cass had to gain the initiative. He made a plan. Like his brother Ben, he had experience in creating newspaper propaganda. He knew just who to invite to his camp for a visit. He set the stage with a few subtle props and extended the invitation.

The reporter scribbled notes as Cass recounted the tale of his search for the Lost Rhoades Mine. They were seated on folding camp chairs, near the fire, in front of Cass Hite's big tent. The mountains towered around them, glorious in spring foliage and the promise of a wonderful summer.

"So what do you have to say now, Colonel Hite? Now that others have found the lost mine?"

"I might be wrong, but I truly doubt the property they located is the mine Enoch Davis has information about," Cass answered coolly. "I do have Davis's map, and the area claimed by Dallin and Hatch is entirely in the wrong area."

"Does that mean there might be other places in these mountains where gold might be found?"

"I don't wish to talk about that at this time," Cass answered. "Our business here is still ongoing. But, I will certainly let you know when I am ready to reveal the true fruits of our explorations."

"I do understand," the reporter smiled. "A good poker player doesn't reveal his hand 'till all bets are on the table."

"Why don't we wash up for supper?" Cass offered. "My hunter killed a fine elk yesterday and we have fresh bread, apricot jam, and Arbuckle's Ariosa Coffee. There's a wash pan on that stump over there with soap and a bucket of water."

As the young man dutifully washed up, he spotted a pile of colorful rocks near the washbasin stump. It was obvious, even to a dude, that the rocks were ore samples. The sly reporter looked around to make sure no one was watching. Then he picked up pieces of the ore to examine more closely.

The following story ran in the Salt Lake papers about a week later.

The Salt Lake Tribune
June 27, 1894
Cass Hite Seems to Have Found
Something Big

Vernal Express: The great gold find near Gilbert Peak is creating the greatest excitement of any find that has been made in the West for years. Lorenzo Hatch and Mr. Holiday were in Vernal this week but would not say much about what they are doing, or what they were going to do. They recorded some new claims, however, and those who talked to them say they are strictly in it.

The Cass Hite party are keeping the secret of their doings to themselves, but a party who visited their camp picked up a piece of rock among some samples in their camp and could see gold in nuggets sticking in the rock, showing that Mr. Hite was on to something better than was first found, and will surprise the mining fraternity when he makes known to them and the community what he has found.

Satisfied that he had smoothed the ruffled feathers of his benefactor, Cass continued the hunt. When the map didn't seem to be working out, he went directly to the Indians like he had done with Hoskininni in Monument Valley.

Dark clouds covered the morning sun. A cool breeze from distant snowfields rippled through the quaking aspens as the men took their seats to begin the parley. Both groups sat on the ground, Indian style, facing each other across the fire.

"This man here is Santawee," the interpreter said. "He ain't much, but he's the closest thing to a chief this band has got. The old man on the right is Tabeeche. He's the holy man, but he don't talk much."

The Indians sat silent, sullen, and angry. The interpreter Cass had hired was a buffalo soldier of the Ninth U.S. Cavalry from nearby Fort Duchesne, a black man in a blue uniform with lots of yellow stripes.

The Indians would not have been there at all, but they had to obey the cavalry soldiers. Cass knew that when he hired the master sergeant and asked him to set up the meeting.

"Tell them I bring presents," said Cass.

He then stood up and handed each of the Indians a blanket.

Santawee cast his blanket aside without looking at it. Tabeeche laid his blanket across his knees without looking at it. Both men kept their gaze fixed on the black sergeant, completely ignoring Cass Hite.

"Tell them I'm a great warrior who killed many blue coat soldiers in the big war between the white brothers."

The black sergeant in the blue uniform turned to Cass and gave him a look that would have scared most other men.

"Tell them," Cass insisted, his eyes dark and determined.

The blue coat soldier dutifully rendered the interpretation in the native tongue.

Neither Indian flinched. They just sat there, glaring at the sergeant.

Cass took his hunting knife from his belt and dramatically presented it to Santawee. "Tell him to keep the knife, and if I lie, he can cut my heart out."

The black sergeant smiled and gave the interpretation.

The Indian reached over and dropped the knife on the previously discarded blanket.

Cass fought to control his anger. "Ask him about the Mormon gold," he said.

The buffalo soldier talked in Utes for a long time but could not coax a response from either of the natives.

"By damn, what does it take with these people?" Cass growled. "Is there someone else we can talk to? Do they have a real chief, someone who can speak for the whole bunch of 'em?"

"Afraid not," the buffalo soldier replied. "All of their big men are dead: Walker, Arapeen, Ouray, even Colorow. All they got left is a few minor chiefs like Santawee and old Tabeeche here."

"Well, let's get the hell out of here," Cass said as he stood up. "This ain't gettin' us nowhere."

Then, a few days later, just when things were looking real bad, a courier on a lathered horse arrived in camp. The man came with a big smile, waving a rolled-up newspaper. "Here ya go, Cass. Old man Rognon said ta get this to ya quick as I could."

As Cass unrolled the newspaper, the headline made him smile:

The Salt Lake Tribune
July 3, 1894
The Strikes at Uintah
Not the Enoch Davis Mine

Vindication at last. The story quoted Mr. Holiday, a partner in the Dallin and Hatch gold claim. It said everyone was now convinced that the gold found by Dallin and Hatch was not the Enoch Davis mine after all. The vein of gold was indeed a rich find, but not the mine Cass had been looking for. The gold was in a dike running east and west near the heads of Ashley Creek and White Rocks Creek.

Mr. Holiday revealed that Dallin and Hatch had found the remains of two men and three horses near their mining claim, killed years earlier in a "hard fight," presumably with Indians. There were articles of camping gear scattered about and the bodies of the men had purposely been burned.

The article then spoke of the Lost Rhoades Mine, "jealously guarded by the Indians," and how several men had vanished over the years while searching for the treasure. Mr. Holiday speculated that the bones found had been from one of those lost prospecting parties and were not the remains of Enoch Rhoades. After this information was revealed, the Dallin and Hatch find became known as Dead Man's Mine.

Cass was thrilled. The Lost Rhoades Mine was still out there somewhere amid other dikes of glorious, gold-bearing quartz. Two treasures to find were better than one.

On August 9, The Salt Lake Tribune had news of Cass Hite. The information came from a letter written by another miner near the Dead Man strike.

Cass Hite tells me he is camped twenty-one miles northwest of our place. He has located some quartz claims there, but is not bothering with placers yet. His belief is that the field is a rich one. Last night he showed me a rock in which I could see the gold with my naked eye. What he has is no fake.

Word of the Dead Man strike and rumors of Cass Hite's success caused a stampede. Newspapers reported that prospectors were pouring into the Uintahs from all over the country. Miners from played-out workings in Nevada and Colorado were flocking to the area. Prospectors from Idaho and Arizona were hurriedly "wending their way" to Vernal.

Men were abandoning the search for gold along the Colorado and Henry Mountains too, seeking their fortunes in the new gold rush, much to Cass Hite's disappointment. The Hite brothers needed their business at Dandy Crossing. The Vernal Express reported, "Traveling expenses are high in this region. Oats are $2 a hundred and hay is $1.50 per bale."

The usual mix of unsavory characters was showing up to take advantage of the miners, too. "Bad men and worse men from Creede, Denver, Cheyenne and Helena," the Salt Lake Tribune reported. "The camp at Dead Man's is the center of attraction, and forty miles west of north of Fort Duchesne is about as tough a place as they make them."

Cass had to deal with a few of the bad men and worse men.

"Don't move you sombitch!"

The sleeping man startled awake and froze solid at the same time. He lay there obediently in his blankets, on his side, his pulse racing, big terrified eyes beneath bushy eyebrows. The cold, steel barrel of Cass Hite's revolver was in his ear.

"I got this other bastard covered, Cass," one of his men called from the other side of the camp. The man was standing straddle of a bedroll with a shotgun pointed at the bushy head peeking out of the blankets. That man, too, lay stiff as a board. Resistance was futile.

Cass Hite made a little speech. "Now, while I got your attention, let me tell you sons-a-bitches one more time. This whole ridge is my claim. You bastards want to find gold you go somewhere else. Me and my team's got this place covered. I ain't gonna tell you again.

Cass then called to a third man standing back by the men's saddles. "Round up their guns, Jack. That's the price they pay for not takin' my advice the first time. We ain't gonna get bushwhacked."

He then looked down at the big-eyed man in the blankets and said, "If you an' your partner are foolish enough to go to the sheriff about this, I'll hunt you down like rabid dogs." He then moved the pistol just a little to the left and pulled the trigger. The big gun spit smoke and flame. Thunder echoed in the valley. Dirt, grass, and pine needles flew through the air. The man squealed like a pig and rolled up in a tight little ball in his blankets, shaking uncontrollably.

"Got them guns, Jack? We better go now. These boys gotta break camp. They got travelin' ta do."

The first rays of morning sun were breaking over the mountains as Cass and his men rode away.

When it came to playing his cards, Cass didn't reveal his hand until September. By then he was ready for the whole world to know.

The Salt Lake Tribune
September 3, 1894
<u>Cass Hite Heard From</u>
He Struck a Fine Belt of Fissures
of Yellow Quartz

The first information concerning Cass Hite since leaving in February last, when he went into the wilderness, after stating to his friends that he was on the trail of a bonanza, was supplied by a letter to a friend, which visited this city yesterday, and which bears postmark of Duchesne Bridge, 1st inst. [September first]

"For many months Mr. Hite says he has been prospecting, pioneering and 'Injuneering' the Uintah range and has found a belt of true fissures filled with nice yellow quartz, the heft of them [most of them] just without the reservation. The latter condition paves the way clear and clean [to legally stake claims]. To perfect locations [file claims] he will spend a month longer before returning to Salt Lake.

Cass had found gold, but it was not the Lost Rhoades Mine. That phantom still eluded him. Enoch Davis had told a tall tale, or he was a lousy maker of maps. Cass wasn't sure which. But it didn't matter now. Cass Hite's future was firmly set in a fine vein of gold-bearing quartz.

Enoch Davis, for his part, was furious. Cass was supposed to find the lost gold and bring it back to save him. He didn't have time for Cass to go off chasing rainbows or digging quartz on some other mountain. His date with the executioner was fast approaching. He vented his frustrations and the newspapers indulged him. The Salt Lake Tribune ran an article on July 30, 1894 in which Enoch Davis complained bitterly about being abandoned by Cass Hite.

Davis was enraged because Cass had never written to him with details of the search as he had promised to do. The condemned man was sure Cass had found the mine and was simply waiting for Davis to be executed so he could have it all. No amount of argument could persuade him otherwise. Davis insisted he had given Hite clear and precise directions to the treasure and hearing no word from Hite could only mean he had been betrayed.

Davis told the newspaper the complete story he had told Hite, about the giant Rhoades, being friends with the old giant's son, a big bowl of golden nuggets and going to the Uintahs with his old playmate Enoch Rhoades. He said he visited the mine, saw the shining walls of gold, and was with his friend when the Indians killed him. He told of his friendship with Cass Hite, how they had agreed to share the treasure, and of the map he had given Hite.

The Tribune reported, "Davis relies upon its discovery [the lost mine] as the only thing that will save him from the sentence that hovers over him, and, having heard nothing from Hite, is almost a mad man at times. With the proceeds from the mine he feels convinced that there is every show for outwitting the executioner, whose dreaded voice he listens for by day and night."

The evening before his execution, the prison warden asked Enoch Davis if he had a last request. He said, famously, "Are there any prostitutes available?"

Having been denied his last request, Enoch Davis was shot and killed by a firing squad on September 14, 1894.

There was no clergy at the execution. Davis said he didn't believe in religion. The warden allowed him to drink whiskey before being shot and all accounts say he was almost too drunk to sit upright on the stool he was tied to. As the time approached, he became ever more loud and profane, pleading that he didn't want to, "die like an Indian." His obscenity-laced pleadings shocked the tender sensibilities of the 500 or so people, men, women and children, who had gathered to watch the state blow a man apart with high powered rifles.

As they put the blindfold on him, Davis shouted for the firing squad to take their (expletive deleted) time, take a good (expletive deleted) aim, and do a good (expletive deleted) job. They did. A newspaper reporter who witnessed the execution said, "Davis died like a dog, the most despicable, mangy whelp that ever met an inglorious fate." Another reported, "His complete lack of nerve might have won him a little human sympathy if it were not for his vile and lying tongue."

Fools Gold

About a month after Enoch Davis bit the dust, someone found his lost mine. It was not the mine Thomas Rhoades had taken his gold from, but it was the mine marked with an "X" on the map Enoch Davis had given Cass Hite.

Salt Lake Tribune

October 26, 1894

<u>The Dead Man's Bonanza</u>

Enoch Davis Myth Exploded at Last

The fabulous Enoch Davis mine is found. Two men, John McCarty and E.H. Brownell, actually traced out the famous mine, found it, examined it – and left it. They left the city on the 19th of July last and only returned to Salt Lake yesterday, crestfallen and disappointed.

By dint of hard struggle and by the use of maps furnished by Enoch Davis and Cass Hite, the men found the exact ledge and traced it to the cave. At first the prophesies of Davis seemed to be borne out, but the men took out their knives and picked off the chunks of gold and bore them out to the light. They were very like gold, but they were not gold, only iron pyrites. With this trifling exception, Davis' vision was verified. The hole was there, the ledge leading up to it, the conglomerate formation of white porphyry, and all that, but nothing more. The ore inside the cave was so brilliant that any mining novice would have taken it for gold.

The men were working for prominent Salt Lake mining attorney E.G. Rognon. Mr. Brownell acted as guide while Mr. McCarty was the mining expert.

The fact that the men were sponsored by E.G. Rognon and using a map "furnished by Enoch Davis and Cass Hite," was a revealing bit of information. When Cass had failed to find the mine in a timely manner, his sponsor, Mr. Rognon, had simply hired another mining expert and a competent guide to seek a second opinion. This while Cass was still in the mountains, tracing the map through the wrong canyon.

Cass was humiliated when he and the rest of the world learned that someone else had found the mine, even though it did prove to be worthless.

After all of the publicity, the public betrayal by his business partner made him look foolish.

But, Cass did get the last laugh. While others had followed the map to the fools' gold, Cass had found the real thing. He had staked several claims on the vein of yellow quartz and it was about to pay off, big time. On the same newspaper page as the article about the fool's gold, a small sub-title read:

Cass Hite's Luck

Messrs. Brownell and McCarty encountered Cass Hite in their travels, and learned that he had just completed a sale to some Denver parties for 18,000 dollars of property in which he had a major interest. Five thousand dollars is up for forfeit and the deal is to be completed on December first. Cass Hite, of course, was feeling happy about the strike.

Cass had done very well. Eighteen thousand dollars was a lot of money. His major interest, even at 50 percent, would be worth about a quarter of a million at modern exchange rates, and it was all tax-free. The United States and Utah Territory had no income tax in those days. Also, the property mentioned might not have been the only claims he sold. He hadn't found the Lost Rhoades Mine, but Enoch Davis had put him on the road to financial recovery.

Snow chased Cass out of the mountains for the winter. Sometime in late October he returned to Salt Lake City.

Wearing his best suit and angry face, Cass strode purposefully into the plush office building and past the young executives who guarded the door to the inner sanctum, the offices of E.G. Rognon, Attorney at Law. One young man stood to bar the door but Cass melted him with a hard look and a cocked and threatening right arm. Cass opened the door and went in unannounced. The office help scattered to find a constable.

Startled by the intrusion, Mr.Rognon looked up from his desk. He then smiled scornfully. "Well, hello Mr. Hite. I didn't expect you back so soon."

Cass was in a rage. "What the hell do you mean sending another man out to follow my tracks and givin' him a copy of my map and all? We had a deal, you... you...."

Rognon cut him off before he could finish. "Be careful, Mr. Hite! Your past legal troubles might be only a precursor of things to come should you get too far out of line, I assure you."

"By damn," Cass growled, moving even closer, "You made me look like a fool. I ain't gonna ..."

Cass was interrupted when a very big man in a fine suit came charging into the room. The big man had a threatening look in his eye and his hand was inside his suit coat. He stammered breathlessly, "Sorry, Mr. Rognon. I had to step outside for a minute. You want me to take this man outta here?"

"I don't think that will be necessary, Mr. O'Grady. Just stand by in case you are needed."

The big man stood very close to Cass, looking down at him with contempt. He was still breathing heavily and his hand still held the pistol concealed by his jacket.

Cass was visibly taken aback. He blinked a couple of times, then turned to Rognon with a look of surprise. Before he could speak the attorney stopped him with a wave of his hand

"Now, Mr. Hite, I have a few things I've been waiting to tell you. First, we do indeed have a deal. As you know, I'm the one who brokered the arrangement to sell the quartz you found. With all I've spent and all I've done, I should get seventy-five percent of the profits, but I will graciously honor our prior signed contract and claim only my agreed upon forty-eight percent. That should make you happy.

"When we consummate this sale, Mr. Hite, the check will be given to you as majority shareholder. But Mr. O'Grady here, and others, who are my representatives, will be at the meeting to escort you back here where we will cash the check together. I will tolerate no deviation from that plan.

"As far as sending Mr. Brownell to find the lost mine, I assure you it was business and nothing more. Your efforts were noble, I am sure, but when, after several months, you failed to properly follow the map, I had no choice but to hire a more proficient reader of maps. I'm sure you understand. Too bad your informant was a fool as well as a scoundrel. That is all I have to say about this matter."

He then nodded toward the door and said, "Mr. O'Grady will see you out."

As Cass obediently turned to the door, Mr. Rognon gave a final, closing remark.

"Oh, and by the way. Mr. O'Grady here will have orders to shoot you if you ever come charging in here like that again. Consider yourself properly warned, Mr. Hite."

Cass Hite was tired and ready to go home. He caught the next train for Green River. He hadn't been to Dandy Crossing since shortly after his fight with Kohler some three years earlier. After two years of musty courtrooms and jailhouses and a third year wallowing in the snowdrifts and mud of the high Uintahs, he was worn out.

Cass wouldn't admit it, but he hadn't been feeling well for a long time. The cold, damp, and high altitude of his recent adventures had aggravated his chronic ailments. He would be 50 in March, if whiskey and his lung troubles didn't kill him first.

In Green River and Hanksville, Cass was still king. Everyone welcomed him home and treated him like a big shot. It was good to be among friends again. The warm sand and sunshine soothed his weary bones and gave strength to his troubled heart.

He found that his little kingdom at Dandy Crossing had shrunk, but it was still a viable business. Hoskininni's gold was supporting more of the operation now. Most of the investor money had dried-up. Ben still had crews actively engaged on the placer bars and the store was making a modest profit. They were being hounded by creditors, but the operation was still afloat, for now.

The thousands of dollars Cass would soon receive for his efforts in the Uintahs would be a godsend. Colonel Ben told him it would be nice if he could find a way to duplicate his success.

The Salt Lake City Gold Rush

After a month or so at Dandy Crossing, Cass and Ben traveled to Salt Lake to complete Cass's business dealings with Mr. Rognon and cash out his claims on the Uintahs. After the paperwork was done, Cass gave a big chunk of the money to Colonel Ben to help prop-up their sagging mining business. The rest he kept for himself. By his reckoning, he had earned it.

Ben went back to Dandy Crossing to pay some bills and rally the troops. Cass stayed in the city. After all he had suffered in the preceding three years, he felt he needed, and deserved, a good vacation.

Cass enjoyed the big city. Living was good there when he had money in his pockets. Money can buy anything, even respectability. Thanks to dearly departed Enoch Davis, Cass had money enough to regain his financial independence and redeem most of his former social standing. His homicidal tendencies and stint in the territorial prison were forgiven him. He was, once again, the wise old prospector who knew everything about mining and the mountains and deserts of Utah.

Cass stayed in Salt Lake through the winter of 1894-1895. His money and notoriety were a big hit with the ladies. He was always in demand at the gentlemen's clubs and invited to all of the social get-togethers. Even the people who served him were comfortable around him. He was a man of sharp wit who could give and take a joke.

On April 3, 1895, The Salt Lake Tribune ran a tongue-in-cheek story about an April fool's joke the chambermaids at Cass Hite's hotel had played on him.

During the evening of April 1st, as Cass was occupied with friends at one of the city's finer clubs, the chambermaids of the Walker Hotel put a dummy in his bed. The girls turned up the gas lamps and left the window blinds open so they could watch from the building next door.

When Cass came staggering in about midnight, he was shocked to find his room cluttered with petticoats, silk stockings, slippers, and women's toiletries. In his bed was the form of a lovely lady with long, curly trusses spread across his pillow.

Cass quickly backed out of the room, went down to the lobby and checked the guest register. Confused, he summoned a hotel porter and asked who had occupied his room. The porter winked knowingly and whispered that he didn't know nuthin' 'bout it.

Cass went to the bar and had a stiff drink, then crept back to the room. He cautiously pulled the bed cover away from the lady's face and found she was only a pillow wearing a wig.

In righteous indignation he summoned the hotel manager and took him to see the dummy in his room. But when they entered, everything was in its place. There was no sleeping pillow lady, no scattered clothing, no women's toiletries, and no other witnesses. Cass Hite was the dummy in the room. The Tribune claimed it was about the best April fool's joke ever played in the city.

A week later, the joke was on Salt Lake City. On April 12, 1895, The Salt Lake Tribune reported that gold had been discovered in Harker's Canyon, just twelve miles southwest of the city.

The news came as a big surprise. Prospectors had combed the region since the Mormons first entered the Salt Lake Valley in the 1840s. Everyone thought the area had been picked over. The Oquirrh Mountains that surrounded Harker's Canyon had been a well-established mining district for more than forty years. Limited amounts of gold and silver had been found in nearby Bingham Canyon, but copper was the dominant mineral.

When word reached Salt Lake of nuggets lying on top of the ground like golden drops of dew, gold fever struck the city like a plague. Newspapers said the find was made by "Buckskin Clark," an old-timer with nearly fifty years mining experience. The gold was placer material, washed down from the mountains and deposited in the dirt of the bench lands and along the streambeds. Buckskin Clark and his associates were feverishly staking claims. In only a couple of days more than a thousand acres had been taken up.

Cass Hite quickly became a key player in the Salt Lake gold rush. In nearly every story filed by The Tribune, his advice was sought and readily given. On April 13 he claimed to have gotten a late start to the new gold fields, having heard about the strike like everyone else. He said when he got to Harker's Canyon in the early morning hours of April 12; he found most of the land already taken. Not to be deterred, he moved to nearby Coon's Canyon and found some terrific placer prospects there. The canyons were full of gold. Cass and his partners located claims on about 600 acres, running nearly two miles up and down the canyon.

Cass told The Tribune:

> I am interested in the placers of the Colorado River, as everyone knows, and wedded to the Uintah Mountains, but this is the first time in a quarter of a century that I have seen anything that brings to me memories of Alder and the Last Chance gulches. Why, it is the biggest thing on earth. [Alder and Last Chance gulches were famous gold strikes in Montana. An estimated $30 million in gold was recovered there between 1863 and 1866].

> Cass continued: Look at this prospect, if there ain't 60 dollars in it I'll eat it, and I want to tell you that it came out of two-thirds of a shovel of dirt. Here is another prospect; not so big, but I took it from another gully, and I am ready to give it as

my opinion that the dirt I saw will run from $25 to $60 per yard. I know that the figures seem extravagant, but I tell you they are correct.

I scraped my best sample from a bank that was certainly less than 100 feet above bedrock and I can't help but conclude that when bedrock is reached the pay dirt will be much higher.

Over the next week, as men like Cass reported their successes, people stampeded from the city to the foothills. They came with every kind of conveyance: saddle horses, buckboards, fringe-topped surreys, freight wagons, pack mules, wheelbarrows and bicycles. The narrow road to the gold field was choked with travelers. To some it looked like the city was being evacuated pending a frightful invasion or natural disaster.

In Harker's and Coon's canyons, the prospecting became a melee. People were running to and fro, examining rocks, digging holes in the ground, arguing, staking claims and jumping claims. Most were total amateurs. Only a few knew how to stake a claim or properly file one.

Cass laughed about a woman seen prospecting with the men, her skirts hitched up to her knees, her frilly hat filled with rock samples. One young man cried like a baby when he could not find the source of a small piece of ore he had found on a hillside.

For most of a week Cass and his prospecting partners were in the field, driving stakes and "perfecting" their claims. They commuted from Salt Lake by carriage in the wee hours of the morning and returned late at night. The pace and fury of the gold rush was maddening. But through it all, Cass always had time to talk to newspaper reporters.

Then, a small paragraph appeared near the end of a Tribune story on April 18. "Cass Hite has been ill the past two days and unable to return to the canyons. He will go out the latter part of the week, however, to commence development on his claims."

It was after midnight when the three men finally arrived at the hotel lobby. They were tired and dirty, but laughing and making jokes like giddy schoolboys. Cass was waiting to greet them wearing his silk robe and slippers with a stout drink in his hand.

"Well boys, how'd it go today?"

"We got that other ridge all staked out, Cass. There were city slickers there already but they didn't know what they was doin'. We put our stakes in right alongside theirs. We sent Bob back to town to get the paperwork recorded before they figure it out. With all the claim markers up there today, the place is a real mess. It'll take the sheriff an' the district court a year or two to untangle all the claims and counterclaims."

"Did you get any offers to buy?"

The three men laughed. "You wouldn't believe it, Cass. Some dude offered old Samuel here a wad a greenbacks that would a choked a alligator. Said he'd give it all for just one claim. Sam looked it over and told him it warn't near enough. The man said to save the claim for him an' he'd go home tonight and sell his house. I'm tellin' ya, Cass, I never seen nothin' like it."

"Like I said," Cass smiled. "There's always more money in sellin' dreams than diggin' dirt."

Other than the old newspaper stories, very little information is available about the Salt Lake City gold rush. To read Utah history it's like it never happened. But, from the newspaper accounts, it appears Cass Hite did very well. He undoubtedly sold his claims while gold fever was still in the contagion stage and quickly left town. On July 12, less than three months after the newspapers reported Cass was developing his Coon's Canyon claims, The Tribune found him returning from the Uintah Basin after a two-month visit. He had abandoned "The biggest thing on earth" - the Salt Lake City gold strike - to go prospecting somewhere else.

There seems to be no record that anyone ever recovered the gold Cass and his friends found in the Oquirrh canyons. Could the whole thing have been an elaborate fraud?

In early May, while the good citizens of Salt Lake were still swarming over the Oquirrh Mountains, searching for the gold Cass assured them was there, he quietly ducked out of town and traveled to Vernal. He went there to investigate a new substance discovered on the Indian lands.

The substance was called Gilsonite, after Sam Gilson, the man who first found a use for the material and developed a market for it. Gilsonite is a naturally occurring resinous hydrocarbon, similar in appearance to obsidian. It can easily be crushed to a fine powder and has been used as a varnish, ink, waterproofing agent, insulating material and a stiffening agent in the manufacture of rubber goods. The mineral is found only in Utah's Uintah Basin and is also known as North American Asphaltum, or natural asphalt.

The Gilsonite business was booming when Cass first got interested. In the late 1880s Sam Gilson had boldly staked claims on the Indian land, then persuaded the federal government to withdraw 7,000 acres of the reservation to make his claims legal. Sam was obviously well connected. By the time

Cass Hite got involved, hundreds of tons of Gilsonite were being mined and shipped by freight wagon, 90 miles south through Nine Mile Canyon to the rail yards in Price. New outcroppings of Gilsonite had been found recently, still within the reservation. Cass was determined to stake his claim on some of those.

But, while Sam Gilson had the political clout to get his claims legalized, that door was closed to others. Cass would have to wait for the reservation to be thrown open to white settlement before he could file claims. To help make it happen, he began using his influence, charm, and money to do everything he could to deprive the Ute nation of their homeland. He was not alone in his efforts. The land was coveted by hundreds of white farmers, ranchers, miners and businessmen.

The Uintah Ouray reservation was established in 1861 by orders of Abraham Lincoln. Brigham Young agreed to give the Utes all of the Uintah Basin because the area was thought to be too cold for agriculture. It was said to be "one vast contiguity of waste, suited only for nomadic purposes and as a hunting ground for Indians." By the 1880s, however, with good farmland becoming increasingly scarce for homesteads, the people of Utah were having second thoughts. Between 1882 and 1909, the size of the reservation was whittled down from four million acres to less than a half million acres.

The Long Road Back to Dandy Crossing

In late summer 1895, Cass went back to his old stomping grounds at Dandy Crossing. After participating in the Salt Lake gold rush and chasing veins of Gilsonite across the Ute reservation, he needed a rest, and maybe a place to hide out.

Things were still limping along in his little kingdom on the Colorado. The biggest news was that his brother John had replaced his nephew Homer as postmaster of Hite. Homer had become disillusioned and was off learning to be a cowboy. The young man had devoted nearly six years to the Glen Canyon gold rush and he was tired of digging holes in the sand and not getting rich. A lot of other people were feeling the same way.

That summer, Hoskininni made one of his visits to see his old friend, Hosteen Pish-la-ki. Cass pulled out all the stops to treat the old chief and his entourage to a good time. He had them camp in a shady grove of cottonwoods, a little removed from his store and post office. He butchered a fatted calf and gathered melons from his garden and fruit from his orchard to provide a feast fit for kings. They exchanged gifts. Cass gave Hoskininni a nice felt hat and a box of cigars from his company store. Hoskininni gave Hite a heavy silver bracelet, with a wise and knowing smile. Cass immediately understood the sentiment and the irony of the gift.

"Ah-hah! Hoskininni is showing Hosteen Pish-la-ki the silver after all," he said. The men had a good laugh.

Cass Hite's blood brother, Hoskininni Begay, was there too. He had become a handsome young man, in his mid-thirties, with two wives and several small children. His long, dark hair was knotted behind his neck in true Navajo fashion and he wore a white man's unbuttoned leather vest without a shirt. A sparkling silver necklace decorated his chest where the vest lay open.

Begay gave Cass a big bear hug, demonstrating his strength as well as his joy to see his white brother. When Cass regained his breath, he took his gold watch from his pocket and placed it in Begay's hand. The Indian couldn't tell time, but he knew it was a valuable gift. All rich white men carried watches on chains, and this one would look good with the chain hanging out of his vest pocket.

Begay took Cass by the arm and led him to the Indian camp. There he untied a beautiful sorrel colt, about a yearling, and put the lead rope in Cass's hand. It was among the finest gifts a Navajo could give, more practical and more precious than silver. Cass graciously accepted the gift.

Cass took the Navajo men into the store and gave them several small presents for their wives and children: colorful cowboy bandanas, buttons, tin cups, matches, coffee, molasses, and hard tack candy.

He took his Navajo guests to see his placer operations near the mouth of Trachyte Canyon. Men were shoveling gravel in the blistering sun and sweating over the mechanical contraptions that swallowed the dirt and spewed forth water and mud. Hoskininni laughed at the thin, weak little ribbon of yellow sand in the bottom of the sluice box.

"You white people are crazy," Hoskininni said. "You work too hard for the yellow sand."

"We are crazy," Cass agreed. "As you once said, it is a disease we have."

"Have you found peace in your heart, my son?"

"Yes, I expect I have," Cass opined. "I've got a little money in the bank and my diggin's are doin' fairly good around here."

Hoskininni smiled to himself. *White men never change.*

As was the Indian custom, the party went on for a few weeks. The Navajos had traveled a long way to pay the visit and they were determined to make it worthwhile. Cass was a good host and indulged every reasonable request.

When the whiskey began to run low, Cass sent Hoskininni Begay and another Navajo all the way to Green River with a note of authorization and a fist-full of dollars to buy more. It was a journey of more than 200 miles that took the Indian delegation four days to complete on horseback. In the meantime, Cass and Hoskininni shot their fancy rifles at a mark, had a horserace or two, and reminisced in the warm glow of friendship and homemade wine.

Hite City about 1898.
Courtesy of the Utah State Historical Society.

One evening Cass entertained his guests by playing his fiddle. The Navajos were intrigued by his magic music box. Most of them had heard musical instruments before but had never been allowed to touch one. When the concert was over, one of the Indians peeked inside the fiddle to see what kind of creature was hiding in there that squealed so pitifully when the bow was drawn over his little wooden cage.

John and the other white men laughed until they cried. Cass was amused, but embarrassed too. "I don't think those savages properly appreciate a true virtuoso of the violin," he said with a sheepish grin. The men laughed even harder.

The next morning when Cass came to the outdoor kitchen for breakfast, John called out, "I put a bread crust and some bacon grease in your fiddle to feed the weasel. You better clean his cage when you get a minute." Again, the men laughed and laughed. Cass suffered it with good humor.

Finally, one morning Hoskininni announced that he was tired of visiting and ready to go home. Within twenty minutes the Indians had struck their camp and loaded everything on their horses to cross the Colorado. Cass bid Hoskininni and Hoskininni Begay a fond farewell and saw them safely on their way across the river.

Back at the store, brother John was grumpy.

"It's about time those injuns left here. They damn near ate all the grub. Any profit we expected to make this summer is long gone. Anything you didn't give 'em as presents they stole. And what was you thinking when you gave that buck your watch? That gold watch musta cost fifty dollars."

"We'll make it all back, little brother," Cass assured him.

Then, with a dark and threatening look in his eye, he said. "Without those Injuns you'd still be keepin' books in St. Lew and somebody else might be runnin' this place. That old man showed me there was gold along this river and a felt hat and a gold watch is a small reward indeed. Anytime those injuns come here and I ain't here to meet 'em, you treat 'em like family, by gawd."

In late October, Cass went back to Salt Lake City to spend the winter. On October 25, The Manti Messenger picked up the following tidbit from the Green River News:

> Cass Hite came up from Dandy Crossing Friday, on his way to Salt Lake City with one thousand dollars worth of gold dust, which has just been extracted from the Ticaboo bar. Jack

Moore and Homer Hite drove in two carloads of cattle from Dirty Devil last week for Mr. Burr. He shipped them to the Denver market.

The Beauty of the Mountains

On January 4, 1896, Utah was officially admitted into the United States as the forty-fifth state. It was a time for celebration. For almost fifty years the Mormons had struggled to have their wilderness kingdom accepted into full fellowship with the rest of the nation. For all of those years, isolationism, polygamy, misunderstood religious zeal and ecclesiastical shadow government had kept the territory apart. Now, with all of those issues hopefully resolved, Utah proudly raised her dark blue flag of statehood.

Cass Hite and his associates rejoiced. Now, by damn, they could finally get out from under those dawdling federal bureaucrats and have their own congressional delegation open the Ute reservation to white settlement. Having many prospects and big plans for the Indian land, Cass and his friends got exuberantly drunk during the statehood celebration.

On January 30, 1896, The Vernal Express borrowed a story from the Salt Lake Tribune and doctored it up a little.

Mining men ... who have been daring enough to invade the Uintah reservation were congratulating themselves last night now that Utah has acquired its full delegation to congress.

The most daring explorer of this region, perhaps, has been Colonel Cass Hite. No man who has returned from its recesses but has confirmed the legend of gold and silver and the companion metals. These stories were known in Zion years ago and it is told of the "Giant Rhoades" that when he periodically returned to Salt Lake City it was with gold nuggets as big as his thumbnail. It was to verify this story that Cass Hite took his life in one hand, a pick in the other, and a belt of cartridges around his waist and went into the district some two years ago. He might not have found the Golconda from which Rhoades obtained his nuggets, but he did find that which has ever made him a zealous advocate of an early opening of the Uintah reservation. With them this morning the Senators take the information that has been acquired by him to demonstrate the necessity for action.

Cass was influencing Utah politics. Letters and maps he provided were going to Washington to help make a case for opening the reservation. There was money to be made and Cass was acting as champion for those who would take the reservation and give each Indian family forty acres and a mule. He could see nothing wrong with his position. Indians didn't value gold and Gilsonite. Why give them land that held those treasures?

And yet, while he had little sympathy for depriving the Utes of their beautiful mountain-land reservation, he secretly harbored a soft spot for the same land, or so he said. In spite of often expressing a dislike for cold, snowy mountains, he claimed he had witnessed paradise in the high Uintahs.

Cass was in his early fifties when he told the following story. He was drinking a great deal and perhaps the tale was born during a quiet alcoholic melancholy. Maybe he was simply waxing sentimental in his declining years. Or, it might be that the story was only a ruse to help push for the opening of the reservation. However it happened, his poetic yearning was just the stuff a newspaper editor, with a hidden agenda, loved.

Vernal Express
February 18, 1897

Reprinted from The Rocky Mountain News:
"I have been in the mountains 30 years," remarked Cass Hite, the veteran prospector, a few days ago. "But the most beautiful scene that ever lay before my eyes was a scene in the Uintah Mountains of Utah. But few white men have ever visited the region, as it is far inside of the Indian reservation and requires a toilsome journey of several days on horseback. In the midst of the mountains is a lake, which surpasses in beauty Lake George, Lake Geneva or any other of which I have ever read a description. The Uintah Lake, which is yet without a name, is destined to attract attention in the years to come from lovers of nature in all parts of the world. The body of water is probably ten miles long and one to three miles wide. On two sides it is shut in by great cliffs that seem to reach the clouds, while at the open end stretches a valley whose beauty no language could describe. The valley is covered in places with

magnificent trees, many of which are 150 feet high and four to six feet in diameter at the base.

"The most remarkable feature about the scenery," continued Mr. Hite, "is the magnificent waterfalls. Three rivers feed from glaciers and immense snowfields far up on the sides of the mountains, and tumble over the face of the cliff. The distance is so great that the water resolves itself into a spray before it reaches the lake, and the Bridal Veil falls are repeated three times in the depths of the Uintahs. It is a scene which can never be forgotten. I have visited every part of the Yellowstone Park, have traveled for days and months in the Grand Canyon of the Colorado, and have stood on the summits of the highest peaks of the Rockies, but nothing I ever saw equals that scene in the heart of the mountains of Utah. The painter who can successfully convey to canvas the glories of that scene will be immortal and his canvas will deserve the best place in the rotunda of the national capitol."

Mr. Hite says that the beautiful lake is only one of 1,000 lakes which are almost linked together for 100 miles into the mountains of Utah. The lakes are supplied with water from the snow-covered peaks and abound in trout. One evening in October 1894, said Mr. Hite, "I stood on the border of the inland lake and saw myriads of trout leaping into the air. The trout were catching a species of fly, which inhabit the region in the fall, first making their appearance in August. The flies swarm by the million over the lakes and as the sun goes down the trout enjoy a feast, which is indeed a rare curiosity. It appeared to me as I looked over the masses of fish plunging through the air that there were fish enough in the lake to supply dinner to the entire 70,000,000 people of the United States."

Who knows? Maybe that lost paradise is still up there in the mountains somewhere. Modern maps don't reveal it, and no one else has ever found it.

The reservation was thrown open in measured increments over the next several years. Men like Cass took full advantage of the opportunities. Prospectors flooded into the former Ute homeland to claim the gold and Gilsonite the Indians had shunned. White men claimed most of the farmland, water, timber, and other natural resources.

Whatever plunder Cass Hite might have gleaned, he sold without occupying the ground. The Uintah Basin was too far north for him. Brigham Young was right. The place was too damn cold.

Gold was discovered in Alaska in 1896 and there was a full-fledged stampede to the Yukon. Cass toyed with the idea of joining the rush, but he just couldn't bring himself to do it.

"What do you think, Colonel Hite? Are you going north to Alaska?"

"I have been considerin' it," Cass said as he ordered another round of drinks.

The men were sitting in a high-class saloon, clean and comfortable, buzzed with alcohol and waxing philosophical. The piano was tinkling a happy little tune as a lovely naked water nymph looked down from a huge oil painting on the velvet-draped wall.

"They say that mountain pass to the gold field is a real killer. You've got to have a whole year's supply of food and clothing before the Mounties will even let you start. You've got to pack all that stuff over the mountain, too, they say."

"So I hear," Cass nodded. "I suppose a man could hire porters."

"A rich man, I guess," one of the men smiled.

"You are a rich man, Cass. Maybe you could hire an Eskimo to give you a sleigh ride to the gold digs. You could be the big dog on the sled while the rest of them pull."

Everyone laughed.

"You know," Cass said with a wistful smile. "If I were a younger man, lean and hungry like when I first came to the Colorado, I'd climb that mountain to the gold fields and drag you other men over the top with me. But shoot, I hate those cold, windswept old mountains. You can't even imagine what it's like spendin' all day fishin' for placers in the icy water of those high mountain streams. And way up there in Alaska where it's dark half the year and the snow never melts? I don't even like to think about it. No boys, I think I'll just hang around here and rest on my laurels."

Cass did get an offer that almost persuaded him join the northbound Argonauts, but it also made him laugh. His friends got a big kick out of it too. The story was reported in The Rich County News on August 6, 1896.

Half a dozen Utah parties have gone to the Klondike gold fields, most of them as representatives of syndicates. Cass Hite, the veteran miner, has been offered $1,000 for his personal services, and an interest in all claims, to pilot a couple of wealthy New York women to the scene of operations. He is considering the offer.

Cass surely had a lot of fun telling that story in the hotels, saloons and brothels of Salt Lake City.

Medicine Man

In early 1900, while staying in Salt Lake City, Cass Hite got sick. This time he was very sick. It looked like he might die.

The doctor made a gloomy prognosis. The alcohol was killing him. Cass was anemic and malnourished - pale as a fish's belly and thin as a snake. For the second time he had developed pneumonia and was fighting for every breath. His heart was seriously weakened and it might quit at any time. To make matters worse, he was giving up inside. It was just too hard to fight. He was tired, discouraged, and despondent.

As he lay in his hospital bed, too weak to raise his head, Cass longed to return to the warm, sheltering canyons of Southern Utah. Visions of his life there danced in his dreams as he labored mightily to breathe, finally surrendering to the darkness as his strength began to fail.

At first he could feel the rhythm more than he could hear it, a steady thumping like the beat of a drum. But the sound was different. The thumping was more of a whoosh, whoosh, whooshing sound. He tried to open his eyes, but he couldn't. He tried to raise himself up, but he couldn't. He just lay there in the dark, with his eyes closed, listening to the rhythm, sliding in and out of consciousness.

Slowly he became aware that his heart was beating to the rhythm. Blood flowed in and rushed out, with a steady, mechanical rhythm. Over the beating of his heart he could hear an animal growling, a wild cat or a badger, a long, long ways off. Slowly the sound became louder and it changed. He could tell it was an Indian singing; a low huffing chant like the singer was working hard, almost out of breath. The chanting was timed to the pace of his beating heart, drawing it out, making it stronger.

Cass could see through his own closed eyes, the figure of an old Indian standing over him. The man was dancing and chanting with a buffalo tail in one hand and a cluster of eagle feathers in the other. He would brush over Cass's chest and face with the buffalo tail, then blow his own chanting breath into Cass's nostrils.

Cass could feel his breathing catching up to the rhythm of his beating heart. They meshed, blood and air, coursing through his veins in the perfect rhythm of the old man's chant. The Indian fanned air toward Cass's nose and mouth with the eagle feathers, then brush his whole upper body with the buffalo tail. Cass looked into the familiar face and recognized Hoskininni.

The next morning Cass slowly opened his eyes and everything was white. He was startled. Was it clouds? Was it heaven? It couldn't be. White is such a cold color. Heaven wouldn't be white. Heaven would be soft and colorful like the warm red sand of Dandy Crossing.

As the whiteness slowly came into focus, Cass recognized it for what it was, the cold, stark walls and ceiling of his hospital room. He lay there for a long time as his head cleared and his vision became more focused. No pretty, sleeping woman in a rocking chair this time. Only bedpans and bottles of pills, sterilizing alcohol, tubes, needles, and syringes. "Better to die than spend a lot of time here," he thought.

He was filled with wonder when he remembered the vision of Hoskininni dancing over him. *What was that all about? Did that really happen, or am I losing my mind?* It seemed so very real. He decided not say anything about it. People might think he was touched in the head.

The doctors were amazed by his miraculous recovery. So were his friends. They had planned an Irish wake and had already bought the whiskey. To their delight and amusement, Cass respectfully declined to participate in his own funeral.

The doctors wanted him to stay in the hospital for another week or two, but Cass couldn't take it. He decided that if he was going to die, he wanted to die on the red rock desert in the little town that bore his name. He was going home to Hite - doctors be damned.

A friend helped him board the train for Green River. He was incredibly weak but equally determined. Wearing a coat with a blanket covering his lap and wrapped tightly around his legs, he sat quietly and watched the pleasant valleys and snow-covered mountains of the Wasatch slide past outside his window. He didn't expect he would ever be back.

Stanton's Folly

At Hite the weather was warmer and the air much cleaner than the winter coal and wood smoke of the big city. Cass was very weak and spent most of his daylight hours outside the cabin reclining in a hammock in the warm desert sunshine. His brother John did all he could for him. John kept him supplied with blankets, pillows, hot coffee, milk and mashed potatoes. Just what the doctor would have ordered.

Things were still plugging along at Hite. There was still some interest in gold mining along the river. John was a good storekeeper and he kept the farm, garden, and orchard flourishing. Colonel Ben was spending more time in the canyon, too. His mother lode of potential investors had pretty well been mined out. Ben was acting as mine foreman now, doing his best to keep the sluice boxes rocking and the bills paid. Hoskininni's gold was carrying the operation, but just barely. There wasn't much profit once the bills were all paid.

The biggest news on the river was the Hoskininni Mining Company. Robert Brewster Stanton, an engineer, had traveled the area in the late 1880s and he was back. Stanton had caught the gold fever from Cass Hite and others while surveying a possible railroad route down the Colorado River. Being a man of vision and ambition, Stanton had helped organize a company whose aim it was to recover the placer gold on a massive scale. No other mining venture along the Colorado had ever been so ambitious.

It was Stanton who named the organization The Hoskininni Company. He had heard the story of how the old Navajo had shown Cass Hite the gold along the river and naming the company after the benevolent old Indian would surely bring good luck.

With a lot of imagination and tens of thousands of investors' dollars, Stanton was building a huge floating dredge. He had set up operations at the mouth of what was becoming known as Stanton Canyon, a couple of miles above Bullfrog Creek. The location was called Camp Stone, after Julius Stone, the president of the company. All of the parts and machinery for the dredge were transported by wagons and carts from the railroad at Green River, a hazardous journey covering 150 miles of primitive dirt roads.

The dredge was a wonder of nineteenth-century technology, a huge floating barge with a long boom extending out the front. Forty-six large metal buckets revolved around the boom like a chainsaw blade. The rotating buckets would carry sand and gravel to a large circular iron screen on the deck where large rocks and gravel were separated and discarded. The fine material would fall into the hold of the barge where amalgamating tables lined with mercury would separate gold from the mud and sand. The floating barge could be moved to almost any location along the river and the miners could live aboard the ship. It was an expensive venture, but a great idea.

The company began putting the barge together in 1897 and spent three years completing the task. It took a long time to build the road and haul all of the nuts, bolts, lumber, and machinery from the railroad. The hull was built onshore and slid into the water on a shipway made of pine logs. The superstructure was added after it was afloat.

The barge was still under construction when Cass went home to die. The big boat was several months away from her maiden voyage, but everyone expected she would be a great success. Cass and his brothers were hopeful. They understood that Stanton's dredge held the key to the future of gold mining in Glen Canyon, sink or swim.

Stanton gold dredge in Glen Canyon – 1901
From *Ghosts of Glen Canyon* by C. Gregory Crampton.

Cass was surprised when he didn't die. In fact, each day on the desert made him stronger and more confident that he could live a few years longer. His mindset changed too. His near-death experience and long hospital stay had given him an opportunity to dry out and he took advantage of it. After forty years with his head in a bottle, he was determined to give up drinking forever.

But, there was a lot of liquor being swilled at Hite, and the close proximity worried him. Men kept offering him whiskey and it might be only a matter of time until one of them caught him in a moment of weakness. He couldn't take the chance.

Then too, Cass found Hite to be unpleasantly crowded. There were too many men, too much commotion, and too many worldly distractions for a recovering alcoholic and a man still regaining his strength after a near-fatal illness. He decided to move to Ticaboo.

In his little cabin at Ticaboo, Cass found the peace and quiet he was searching for. It was a lonely place, but lovely, too. He broke ground for a garden and tinkered with his gold pan at the water's edge whenever the notion took him. He enjoyed his own company and he experienced a renewed appreciation for life. He also had time to think. He began to ponder the age-old questions of what life is all about.

In the years to follow, Cass didn't leave Ticaboo often. His days of spending winters in nice hotels were at an end. For one thing, he didn't have the money to do that anymore. Whiskey, gambling, women, and the burdens of running his mining empire had consumed his fortune as well as his health. Besides, his change of lifestyle had taken away the big city's appeal. How would a single man spend time in the city if he didn't drink?

For months the vision of Hoskininni dancing over him while he was sick haunted him. Did it really happen? He wasn't sure. While living with the Indians he had witnessed the old medicine man casting spells and healing sick people with his sand paintings and chants. He had witnessed Hoskininni apparently leaving his body to go somewhere else to scout for game or answer questions about what the white men were up to. He knew the old man possessed some strange powers.

After brooding about it for a time, he decided to visit the reservation and seek out the old warrior. He was feeling much better now. The weather was pleasant and the journey would do him good. And, he smiled, this time Hoskininni could act as host.

Cass stopped at Hite and told his brothers where he was headed. He took some items from the shelves of the store and tucked them safely in his saddlebags. When storekeeper John complained, Cass set him straight. It was okay to give Hoskininni's family presents from the store. They were partners in the business, damn it.

As Cass stepped up in the saddle to go, John walked over to bid him farewell. As Cass took the horse's reins, John said with an impish grin, "got yer fiddle?"

Cass sat on the horse looking down at John with hard, cold eyes. Then he smiled, turned the horse and started for the river crossing.

A Navajo sheepherder spotted the white man coming from a long way off and sent his young son on a pony to alert the camp. As Cass approached he could see they were expecting him. The women and children were all out of sight and half-a-dozen men loitered about innocently, with rifles leaning against trees and doorways to be close at hand.

As he rode into the camp he was recognized and a great shout went up. People came tumbling out of the hogans and from the shelter of the sand dunes a hundred yards away. Hoskininni came running, beckoning him to get down from the horse and come to the fire. Cass tipped his hat to the ladies and saluted the warriors with a raised fist. They all crowded around as he stepped down from the horse and a young man stepped forward to take his reins and lead rope. Cass was overwhelmed by the reception.

A young girl rekindled the fire while women scurried to prepare food. Cass and Hoskininni sat on opposite sides of the fire and smiled at one another. Cass noticed that Hoskininni really was an old man now. Hoskininni noticed that Cass was much healthier than the last time he saw him. All of the people noticed the bulging panniers on Cass's packhorse and wondered what fine presents he might have brought them.

The men ate, exchanged gifts, and then talked late into the night. Hoskininni Begay was not at the camp. He had gone south to Kayenta to visit relatives. Cass was disappointed, but it did give him more time to talk to Hoskininni alone.

In the early morning hours, with the sparkling Milky Way dividing the night sky and the orange embers of the fire glowing soft and still, Cass finally was able to have the old man all to himself.

From the shadows of the campfire, Hoskininni looked old and small. He was probably in his nineties by then. His long hair was streaked with white. His face was wrinkled and etched with the scars of smiles and sadness and a life lived out-of-doors.

"Are you well, and are you happy?" Cass asked the old man.

Hoskininni looked up and smiled. The question took him by surprise. No white man had ever been concerned about his health and happiness before.

"My heart is at peace," the old chief said.

"Your family doesn't seem to be doing as well as before," Cass said, probing the bounds of their friendship. "The children are ragged and you don't have as many horses and blankets."

"Yes, we are poor," Hoskininni agreed, seeming not to be offended by the cutting remark. "We have but little meat to serve an honored guest. In the old times we would have raided the Mexicans or taken new horses from the white men beyond the San Juan. But we can't do that now. We buy food from the white people when our corn doesn't grow. They end up with our blankets, silver, and horses."

The two men sat looking at one another other across the embers of the fire. They could read each other's thoughts, but neither of them spoke. It would have been a futile conversation and they both knew it.

Cass was wondering why the old man still wouldn't reveal the source of the silver. It could greatly alleviate the poverty on the reservation. Hoskininni, on the other hand, looked into Cass Hite's eyes and still recognized a spark of greed there. The white men could never understand. The land, be it only sand, red rocks and sage, was a holy place, more precious than silver and the white man's goods.

Finally, Cass dropped his eyes and changed the subject.

"I have been very sick," he said.

"I know," Hoskininni answered, very matter-of-fact.

"I saw you in a dream," Cass added.

Hoskininni only smiled.

"In my dream you were standing over me, and you were blessing me in a sacred way."

"Have you found peace in your heart, my son," Hoskininni asked.

"I was dying and you brought me back," Cass whispered.

"Sometimes a man should live a little longer to catch up on things he has missed in this life," Hoskininni said. "You have been given a gift, my son. What will you do with it?"

"I have stopped drinking whiskey and I have made peace with the Mormons," Cass offered.

"That is well, my son. Search your heart and see what other things the creator might want you to do."

Cass left the Navajos a few days later to return to his garden and gold pan at Ticaboo. Several of the Navajos, including old man Hoskininni, rode with him all the way to Dandy Crossing to see him safely back across the river. Cass was grateful and he enjoyed their company. As they parted ways on the bank of the Colorado, Cass reached out and took the old chief in the grip of brotherhood and said, "Thank you, my adopted father. You have twice saved my life."

"Only once," Hoskininni corrected. "You would never have found the silver." Both men laughed as they turned their horses to depart in separate directions.

Maggie May

The angel of mercy came home to her little house in Hanksville. Her name was Mrs. Bicknell now, and her husband and adopted family came with her. Cass heard she was in town and stopped by to see her, even though she was now a happily married woman. Her husband was at work so they visited out in the yard, by the picket fence, along the street where all of the neighbors could witness that everything was on the up and up.

The woman's children were playing in the yard. There were three of them all together, all of them girls, ranging in age from about ten to fourteen. The youngest little girl had dark hair and dark eyes. Her mother called her over.

"Mr. Hite, I want you to meet Maggie," the woman said, and as she said it, there was a special look in her eyes and a special sound to her voice. Cass understood immediately and he broke out in a cold sweat.

"Maggie, this is Mr. Cass Hite. He is a good man who lives way down by Dandy Crossing on the Colorado River."

"How do you do, Mr. Cass Hite," the little girl said with a shy, innocent smile.

Cass's words caught in his throat and he had to try twice before he could say, "I am fine, young lady. You are as pretty as your mother."

"Thank you, Mr. Cass Hite," said Maggie with a stiff curtsey and a flush of color to her cheeks.

"How old are you, honey?"

"Nine years old and I'll be ten at Christmas time."

Cass and his one-time caregiver locked eyes and volumes of unspoken words passed between them. Cass had suspected, but now, finally, he knew for sure.

"Maggie, why don't you go to the house and bring Mr. Hite a glass of cool water?" The woman suggested.

As the child went on her errand, Cass said quickly, "Things get lonesome down on the river. Can I write to her?"

"Not until she writes to you first," the woman insisted.

"I'll give her a reason," he said.

After he drank the best glass of water anyone had ever offered him, Cass walked to the little store in town, returning a short time later with a bag of candy. He called all of the children over and gave each of them a peppermint stick under the watchful eye of their mother.

As he was handing out candy and talking to the children, a man walked up and stood watching suspiciously. The woman beckoned for the man to come closer.

"John, this is Cass Hite. Cass, meet my husband, John."

Cass cautiously extended his hand. John Bicknell took it with cool indifference.

"Nice to meet you, Mr. Bicknell. I do hope you don't mind my speaking to your wife out here by the street like this. It's just that your good wife here saved my life a few years ago when I was dying of pneumonia and I feel a true sense of obligation to thank her every chance I get."

"Yes, she told me about that," the man said coldly.

"I do hope you will forgive me for giving your children candy. There is so little I can do to repay my debt to this whole community."

"That is all right," the man said.

There was an awkward pause.

Finally, Cass said, "You're a lucky man, Mr. Bicknell. You have a lovely family."

"Thank you, sir."

Silence filled the air again. Cass couldn't think of anything more to say. The three girls stood innocently looking up at him, quietly munching their candy. Mr. and Mrs. Bicknell stood together holding hands, graciously suffering the indignity of his presence.

It was time to go.

"Well, I must be on my way," Cass said formally. "I have things to do before I start for Green River in the morning."

"Good day, Mr. Hite."

"Good day to you, Mr. Bicknell, Ma'am, children." Cass tipped his hat, turned on his heel and walked away without looking back.

About a week later, as Cass was passing through the store and post office at Hite, his brother John hailed him. "Got some letters here for you," he said.

The letters were from the Bicknell children. Cass sorted through them until he found the one he wanted. He opened it carefully and reverently. The script was very neat and well organized, the perfect handwriting for a proper young lady. The letter read:

"Dear Mr. Hite. Thank you for the candy. I like cats and horses. Do you have any cats at your house? Love, Maggie."

Cass went for a walk along the river. When he came back to the store he said to his brother John, "That old cat had kittens a while back. I'm gonna take one of 'em back down ta Ticaboo with me. Got some damn mice in the house."

With that letter, Cass opened a regular correspondence with Maggie that lasted for the rest of his life.

The Bank of Ticaboo

The Hite brothers knew that the future of gold mining on the Colorado depended a great deal on the success or failure of Robert Stanton's dredge. If the machine proved to be successful, the value of their placer claims might be greatly enhanced. If it didn't work, it might signal the end of commercial gold mining on the Colorado. Colonel Ben, being a practical man, began looking for other ways to make a living, just in case. He invested in a new enterprise in Texas, and began fishing for an alternative livelihood along the river. He decided copper mining might be just the thing.

Copper had been found in the early days of prospecting on the Colorado, but with gold promising much higher returns, no one bothered to mine copper. It would be difficult to market copper in the rugged red rock country. Roads were primitive and distances were extreme. It would cost a great deal to set up a smelter in the canyons, and hauling raw ore in freight wagons to an established smelter in Colorado or central Utah would be too expensive.

Colonel Ben was hopeful anyway. What the heck? Maybe he could file claims on the copper and sell the claims. That plan had worked in the gold fields, why not the copper fields?

On December 20, 1900, The Salt Lake Herald ran a story about Colonel Ben Hite and his copper prospects near Dandy Crossing.

After a whole season's campaign at his different properties along the Colorado River, Colonel Ben Hite arrived in the city yesterday and tomorrow will start for San Antonio, Texas, for a six weeks roundup of his interests in the vicinity of that place.

The Colonel reports, as the chief feature of interest in the section from which he came, the opening up of some remarkably fine copper propositions. Lodes have been discovered, he says, covering a stretch of eighteen miles from Dandy Crossing down the river, and he looks for the opening of some very good copper mines down there. At numerous other places copper has been found and the chances are that it will not be long till copper mining will be attracting as much or more attention than placer gold mining is now receiving.

His brother Cass, he says, has put in the whole season with him and he is now, what the Colonel describes as a rejuvenated man, enjoying better health than for years.

In 1901 the Stanton dredge was put to work and she was a marvel to behold. The concept was right. The design was right. The science was right. The engineering was right. But the gold was wrong. The floating behemoth just couldn't catch the gold dust in the sand. The gold was too fine. Try as they might, the gold washed away with the muddy water.

The equivalent of three million dollars had been spent on the floating treasure box and all of the tweaking of machinery and cursing and praying by the crew couldn't fix the problems. After a few months of humiliating good effort, the big barge was abandoned at her berth along the river and the investors went home broke. The Stanton dredge was the biggest shipwreck in Glen Canyon history. The Colorado River gold rush sank with her.

The mining companies pulled out after Stanton's failure. The moneymen, dreamers and schemers all went home. Gold mining along the river was reduced to a few individual die-hards engaged in subsistence mining. Those who stayed were the hard core of the prospecting fraternity, independent souls who would rather make a dollar a day with a gold pan than work for a taskmaster somewhere else.

With no hope of future investors, the Hite brothers were forced to liquidate their holdings. Hoskininni's gold was too expensive to mine. The house of cards finally collapsed. The brothers shut down their struggling commercial placer operations and sold everything they could. Some dreams die hard.

In spite of the economic collapse, Cass wouldn't let go of Dandy Crossing and Ticaboo. Those places were home. Where else would he go? The canyons of the Colorado had nurtured, sheltered, and defined him for more that twenty years. Now, like Hoskininni's Monument Valley, those places were sacred, more precious than silver and gold. He was beginning to understand the Native American mindset.

Colonel Ben collected his share of the crumbs of the empire, packed his bags and caught a train for Texas. John chose to stay and keep the store and post office open. The keeper of the books resolved to hunker down and wait for the next mining boom. Or, just maybe, someone would decide to build a railroad bridge at Dandy Crossing and he would be sitting on some prime real estate. Who could guess?

Cass hung up his spurs as mining superintendent and went back to what he knew best, prospecting and panning gold. His fortunes had gone from boom to bust but he still had his dreams. For the next dozen years the former king of the Colorado would be the wise old hermit of Ticaboo, the sage and oracle for the independent miners all up and down the river.

The Crescent Saloon in Green River was a hot, muggy place that afternoon. The barkeeper had wet dishtowels hanging from the open windows to help keep the flies out and cool the place down some. The covered windows made the place dark inside, but it was a good attempt at evaporative air-conditioning.

Cass Hite was sitting at the bar, chewing a cigar and sipping a Sarsaparilla.

A man came in knocking dust off his hat against his pant leg. He stopped and squinted for a moment as his eyes adjusted to the dim interior of the room, then he sat down next to Hite.

"Old Hickrey," the man nodded to the bartender. Then, turning to Cass, he said, "What you drinkin' old hoss? Let me buy ya somethin' ta wash yer mouth out with."

Cass gave the man a look that almost knocked him off the barstool. "I don't drink, damn it!"

"It's okay Cass," the bartender intervened. He's new in town and he don't know any better."

The new man gave both of them a bewildered look and said, "Sorry boys, I didn't mean no disrespect."

"This here's Cass Hite," the bartender said. "He's drunk more whiskey than Niagara Falls, but he give it up a couple a years ago. He just stops in here to visit with me once in a while cause we're real good friends. Ain't that right, Cass?"

Cass nodded, then spit a wad of chewed-up cigar at the spittoon.

"Are you really Cass Hite?" the new man asked.

"I am."

"I heard about you. People say you found more gold than the pearly gates a heaven."

Cass didn't respond.

"Some people say you're the smartest and the luckiest gold miner that ever lived. I always wondered if it was true."

"Hell yes it's true," the bartender interjected. "Cass here's got more gold than Teddy Roosevelt's got teeth. He was just tellin' me 'bout his private bank."

Turning to Cass, the bartender smiled and said, "go ahead Cass, tell this man 'bout that private bank of yours. He's never heard the story."

Cass was smiling as he took another swig of his soda pop.

"I never met a man who owned a private bank," the new man said. "I surely would like to hear about it."

"It's called The Bank of Ticaboo," Cass began with a grin that raised the curled tips of his moustache to the lower level of his ears. "I'm the only one with money in my private bank, and the bank itself is two hundred yards wide and over half-a-mile long."

The new man gave the bartender a doubtful look and rolled his eyes toward the ceiling. "Listen to him," the bartender laughed. "He's tellin' you the truth."

"The Bank of Ticaboo is the big gravel bar in front of my cabin down on the Colorado," said Cass, still smiling. "All the gold I will ever need is there, in the sand, where bandits and bankers can never steal it. When I need a little money, I just take my gold pan down to the water's edge and make a withdrawal."

Old Dogs Still Bite

Cass was growing old, but his reputation as a man of action didn't age. Younger men still treated him with a great deal of respect. Most were even a little afraid of him.

It was late afternoon when sixteen-year-old Ruben Turner rode his horse down the rough wagon road in Trachyte Canyon. It was his first trip to Hite, but he knew he was approaching his destination. Trees, corrals, fields and fences were the first signs of civilization the boy had seen in the fifty miles since leaving Hanksville. As he approached the cabins he could see several men sitting at a long, rough-cut board table under a bowery playing cards. The men were laughing and joking with one another.

The young man turned the mail pouch over to postmaster John, then walked over to see what was going on. He had been riding all day and he would stay the night before starting back to Hanksville in the morning.

There were eight men at the table. Several bottles of whiskey and a few firearms were on the tabletop with the cards. Most of the participants were obviously drunk and the party was dangerously unruly. As the boy approached, one of the rowdies looked up from his cards and said, "Hello there, kid. Come over here and have a drink."

"No thank you, mister."

"Get over here and have a drink!"

"No thank you, mister. I don't drink."

"You will today," the drunk growled as he stood up. "I offered you a drink and by damn you better get over here and have one."

"I don't want no drink, mister," the boy said as he began to back away.

The bully surged forward, grabbed the boy and wrestled him to the ground. Then, holding the kid down, he tried to force whiskey down his throat from a bottle.

An old man with a clubbed foot reached out with his cane to snag the drunken troublemaker in the crook of his arm, pulling him back and allowing the boy to break free. Some of the whiskey was spilled in the process.

"Why, you crippled old bastard," the drunk bellowed as he stood up. "Nobody crosses me like that. Nobody!" He took a couple of quick steps to the table and reached for his pistol there by his cards.

"FREEZE!" came a command that stopped everyone in their tracks.

Old man Cass Hite was standing a few feet away with his hand on his revolver, still in its holster. The look on his face would have melted the polar ice caps. Everyone froze in place. Not a breath of air or a blinking eye disturbed the sudden quiet.

Suspended in frozen animation, the drunken bully stood bent over the table with his hand on his pistol. He looked up at Cass and the fire in his eyes melted to wisps of thin smoke. The fight went out of him. Very carefully he moved his hand away from his gun and stepped back from the table.

"Pack yer shit and get out of here, Bill," said Cass in a clear, cold tone of voice. "Come back some time when you can behave more civil."

The humiliated bully swelled up in his chest and beat his eyelashes hard like there was something he just had to say, but then he thought better of it, turned his back and walked away.

Turning to the kid, Cass said, "Come with me boy and I'll show you where you can sleep tonight. Have you had any supper?"

As they walked away, the men at the table began to breathe again. They quietly gathered up their whiskey, cards, and firearms and scattered to their respective beds for the night.

The Ghosts of Glen Canyon

The canyons of the Colorado grew quiet in the early years of the twentieth-century. The old prospecting camps lay empty and silent. Gone was the clink of shovels on gravel, the joyful splash of muddy water falling from a sluice box, the lusty shout of excitement as a bone-weary boy in patched overalls spotted a wee drop of yellow in his gold pan.

The big river flowed indifferently past sandbars bearing outdated claim markers and abandoned old cabins. Brief summer showers did their best to fill holes in the sand dug with such toil and sweat only a few years before. White cotton ball clouds dragged silent shadows through empty canyons. Coyote tracks topped the dust on the old Trachyte road.

Colonel Ben Hite died in Wichita, Kansas in October 1906. He had abandoned Texas by then and moved on to greener pastures. He was buried far from Dandy Crossing in a place where cemeteries are covered with grass, well watered by gentle rain.

Cass and John Hite remained on the river, the last remnants of the pioneer breed. Cass still worked his sluice box and John was doing a little business at the store. Homer never came back. He played cowboy for a few years then migrated to Salt Lake to work for a newspaper.

The Glen Canyon copper prospects did produce a little fruit, but not for Colonel Ben. In 1906 Benjamin Harshberger was attempting some serious copper mining in the White Canyon area. He constructed a ferry at the mouth of North Wash, near the ruins of Crescent City, the old mining camp of Adolph Kohler. Harshberger starved out in just a year or two. No one could afford to haul raw ore across the desert.

In October 1907 a group of river runners stopped at Ticaboo. They stayed overnight and watched Cass work his sluice box before continuing down the river. The Bank of Ticaboo was still loaning Cass a little money.

In January 1908, The Salt Lake Mining Review ran the following article:

> "Colonel Cass Hite, so well known in Salt Lake a number of years ago, when his statuesque figure was a familiar sight on Zion's streets, is sojourning at Hite post-office, Garfield County, Utah, on the Colorado River, where he is steadily engaged in the operation of the Ticaboo bar gold placer diggings. Colonel Hite writes a Salt Lake friend that he is having a goodly measure of success in his mining operations, and that preliminary work has been so far advanced that he can now go on with regular sluicing."

Cass was working alone, finding almost enough gold to justify the effort. It was hard work for an old man. A couple of times a year he would travel to Green River or some other town to trade his gold dust for supplies and a few greenbacks to put in his wallet.

Ticaboo was a lonely place, but Cass didn't mind. He wasn't totally isolated. Whenever the notion took him he made the fifteen-mile trip to visit his brother John at Hite. When mail came for Cass, John would send someone to deliver it, or he would go himself. To amuse himself, Cass subscribed to a few newspapers and magazines, wrote faithfully in his journal and played his fiddle.

Cass enjoyed playing his fiddle, especially when he was by himself in Ticaboo. With no audience of music critics to satisfy, he could indulge himself in uninhibited freedom of expression, his music reverberating in the echo chamber of the ledges.

Sometimes he would sing. After days on end with no one to talk to, it felt good to belt out a rowdy rendition of *Ole Suzannie* and hear his own strong voice coming back as an echo. He smiled when coyotes joined him in a duet. Some coyotes sang with his music, others barked harsh criticisms from the shelter of distant sand dunes. Cass didn't mind. Coyotes were jokesters in Indian mythology. One should never take them seriously.

The desert ravens were more polite. The ravens would come to the sound of his music and sit in the ledges near his cabin. Between songs he could hear them applauding with their gurgling chirps and clicking noises. He knew they would clap if only they had hands. When his recital was finished, Cass would bow to his audience of desert creatures, then exit his open-air concert hall to hang the violin back on its peg in the cabin.

Cass Hite – 1912. Courtesy of the Utah State Historical Society

Cass enjoyed writing letters, and one of the greatest joys of his life was his regular correspondence with Maggie May. His secret daughter wrote faithfully, and through their exchange of letters he was able to share her growing up years as she passed from little girl, to giggling teenager, and finally a fine young woman.

Cass could never bring himself to tell her he was her father. He didn't feel it was his place to say it. He didn't think her mother ever told her either. The young lady was forever Margaret Bicknell, a compassionate, sweet young woman who corresponded with a lonely, notorious old hermit who lived way down on the desert somewhere. They were improbable pen pals, nothing more.

In her innocence, Maggie invited Cass to her wedding, but he didn't go. He didn't want to spoil the special day for the two women who meant the most to him. He stayed at Ticaboo instead, witnessing visions of the ceremony in his daydreams.

Oh Lord, what might have been.

At the Bank of Ticaboo, Cass usually worked a few hours in the mornings and another hour of two in the late afternoon. In the heat of the day he sought the shade of the cottonwood trees near his cabin.

It surprised him one morning as he was walking down to his gravel digs, to see a horse and rider across the river near Red Canyon. He stopped and shielded his eyes from the early morning sun, trying to better see who the rider might be.

It quickly dawned on him that the man was an Indian, an old Indian. Not an Indian that was old, but an old-time Indian. The man was sitting a magnificent horse and his legs, chest, and arms were bare, the way the Indians from the 1840s and '50s had been. There was no trace of white man's clothing or weaponry that Cass could see. The man's long black hair was tied in a knot with a cord behind his neck, Navajo style, and a gleaming silver necklace caught the morning light and glistened like sparkling water.

As Cass stood transfixed, the Indian held his clenched fist high in the air in a warrior's salute, and the sound of his triumphant yell echoed in the ledges. The sound of it sent chills through Cass that literally shook him to his core.

The Indian turned the beautiful horse and raced away, out of sight into the tangle of hills and canyons across the river, toward the rising sun. Cass found his heart racing and his breath coming quick. *Who was that?* But, he thought he knew, even if he didn't want to think it. Later he checked his calendar and recorded the date. It was October 30, 1909.

A few days later his suspicions were confirmed. Hoskininni Begay came to his cabin in the evening time. He had crossed the river near Red Canyon to avoid the white man settlement at Hite. He brought with him a medicine blanket that he somberly presented to Cass. It was indeed, confirmation that the old chief had died. It was a time of grieving, so Hoskin-Begay didn't speak. He placed his hand on Cass Hite's shoulder and bowed his head for a time, then turned, remounted his horse and went back to cross the river. Cass didn't have a chance to tell him about the apparition he had witnessed.

Cass placed the folded blanket on the foot of his bed and sat in silence for a while. He then went to his old steamer trunk and dug out his copy of the poem Cy Warman had written while sitting on the bank of the Colorado back in 1893.

The Ghost of Hoskininni

They tell the tale of the Ticaboo
Beyond the snowy range,
A story if it be not true
Is surely wondrous strange.

They say at midnight when the winds
From out of the canyons blow,
And Colorado's foaming waves
Dash on the rocks below.

A horse of solid silver comes
Whose feet are shod with gold,
And dashing o'er the canyon walls
Is reined by rider bold.

The ghost of Hoskininni
With wild and wandering eye,
Who comes to guard the pathway
'Gainst the Hosteen Pish-la-ki

The sheep men tell the story
The prospectors who came,
From the Tintic mines in Juab
Say they have heard the same.

The trapper by the river
My guide the Navajo,
Says he has heard the story
And knows that it is so.

That every night at midnight
When winds go wailing by,
Rides the ghost of Hoskininni
'Gainst the Hosteen Pish-la-ki

For here it was the Spaniard
He said made Injun slave,
And maybe so the river
Flows sometimes by the grave.

Of my own mother's mother
Who fore she came to die,
Was made to dig the Peso
For the Hosteen Pish-la-ki.

But brave old Hoskininni
Fore death his hands had tied,
Said he would guard the Peso
Made paper talk and died.

And even now at midnight
As we talk you and I,
Rides the ghost of Hoskininni
'Gainst the Hosteen Pish-la-ki.

Hoskininni died at the end of October and almost immediately winter set in. It turned out to be the coldest winter anyone in Glen Canyon had ever experienced. With the cold weather, Cass's health began to fail again. His lung troubles returned and he was suffering with bursitis.

Salt Lake Mining Review
February 15, 1910

The weather on the Colorado River is the most severe ever known since the diggings were first discovered. The river is frozen over and there is eight inches of snow where snow was never known to stay more than a few hours. Cass Hite still holds on to his property on the river. He has leased the Ticaboo property there.

It was a tough thing for Cass to lease his Bank of Ticaboo, but he just couldn't shovel gravel anymore. He would be 65 in March and his bursitis and lung ailment were keeping him close to the cabin. Tending his garden was about all the work he could do. In spite of leasing his gold claim, Cass remained at his cabin at Ticaboo. There is no evidence that anyone actually worked the claim after Cass Hite gave it up. By 1910 the Colorado River gold rush had pretty well run its course.

A few months earlier, a kindred spirit had moved in across the river from Cass. Bert Loper was a young man, just forty years old, a river rat who had fallen under the spell of the Colorado. Like Cass, he was an independent soul who hated to work at the bidding of others. He had come to join those hardy pioneers who eked out their livelihood in the glorious self-governance of a gold pan and a dream. He had been a member of the river running party that stayed overnight with Cass back in 1907. That visit and Cass Hite's influence was his inspiration. Bert Loper wanted his own Bank of Ticaboo.

Loper leased a claim from a man named Adams, near the mouth of Red Canyon, about three miles upstream and on the opposite side of the river from Ticaboo. There was a fine cabin on the property. Loper christened it, "The Hermitage."

Bert became a subsistence miner, like Cass, with a garden and a sluice box. Like most of the gravel bars along the river, the claim near Red Canyon had shown a little color over the years but had failed to make anyone rich. Loper harbored no dreams of grandeur. He hoped only to make an independent living.

Bert and Cass became friends. Bert would row his boat across the river to visit once in a while, and the men would trade stories, magazines, and garden produce. They enjoyed their visits together, but they also enjoyed living apart. Loper found Hite to be frustratingly opinionated in his old age. Cass found the younger man to be annoyingly naïve and idealistic. The two hermits had quarrels about politics and religion that kept them from speaking to each other for months at a time.

However, they were able to patch things up when they needed each other's help. Bert was able to borrow money from Cass to travel to Salt Lake to get his teeth fixed. Bert ran errands for Cass and hauled him around in his boat.

"Hello, Cass Hite," Bert Loper called as he approached the cabin. He always tried to give the old man a "heads up" that he was coming. Cass was a relic of the pioneer times and carried his gun everywhere. Bert had surprised him once and got to see the business end of that sawed-off hand cannon. He considered himself lucky that he wasn't killed. Cass told him after that to always be sure he hollered or threw a rock or something before he got to the cabin. Bert followed that advice, but it was tough when the old man was hard of hearing.

"Who goes there?" Cass called from inside the cabin.

"It's me. Loper."

"That you, Loper?"

"It's me, Cass. Don't shoot damn it. I got those things from the store you wanted."

"Come in, Loper. I was just fixin' supper. I'll put another cup a water in the stew. How's that?"

"Didn't come to eat, Cass. I brought that liniment you wanted. I got some coffee, sugar, hardtack, and some magazines, too. Your change comes to eighty-seven cents. You want me to put it in your biscuit tin?"

"Keep it," Cass offered. "It was nice of you to get that stuff for me."

"Thank you," said Loper. "Find any gold this week?"

"Naw, I ain't been feelin' too good. I did hoe my tomatoes though. How's things in town?"

"Same ol' stuff. I did hear they passed that sixteenth amendment. The income tax is law now."

"They can't do that!" Cass snarled. "It's unconstitutional. They can't take my money just 'cause I earned it. This'll cause another civil war. I'll shoot the government buzzard who comes here to take my money."

"Oh settle down, Cass. It's not that bad. The people all agreed. They passed the amendment. We have a democracy. We need taxes to run the country."

"You're an idiot, too."

"There you go. Everything's always got to be personal with you."

"Taxes are personal. If you're afraid them damn senators don't make enough, go give 'em your money. Better yet, you send 'em that eighty-seven cents I just gave you."

Bert slammed the money down on the table. "You don't ever have to give me anything, you grumpy old goat."

"Take yer income tax and get the hell outta here," Cass growled.

"Glad to do it," Loper snapped as he stomped out of the cabin.

There was another neighbor, too. Alonzo (Lon) Turner lived about 18 miles downstream at the California Bar. He, too, was a subsistence miner. Glen Canyon was becoming crowded with hermits.

On February 22, 1914, Lon Turner was traveling up the river to Hite. The weather was cold so he stopped to spend the night at Ticaboo with Cass Hite. He hailed the cabin as he approached and didn't get an answer. He knocked at the cabin door and didn't get a response. Thinking Cass had probably gone to Hite to visit his brother John, Turner opened the door and went in, planning to spend the night in the other man's cabin, as was the custom of travelers along the river.

Lon Turner found Cass in his nightclothes, lying on the floor dead. Turner hiked up the river three miles to a point across from Bert Loper's cabin and fired his pistol in the air to attract Loper's attention. Knowing something was wrong; Loper rowed his boat across the Colorado and had a parley with Turner. Then Loper, being the younger man, hiked the fifteen miles to Dandy Crossing in the cold and dark of night to give the news to John Hite.

A burial party returned to Ticaboo the next day. They found Cass's journal on the table. The old prospector had made his last entry on February 15. He had missed celebrating his 69th birthday by two weeks.

Cass had told his brother John and others, that when it came his time to go, he wanted to be buried at Ticaboo. He said he liked it there and would be happy to remain forever. The men dug a grave about 200 feet east of the cabin door, wrapped the old prospector in a blanket and buried him there.

Cass had probably been dead about eight days when his friends dug his grave. They didn't have lumber or time to prepare a proper casket, and no one made mention of any type of religious observance. Sometime later a fence of rough planks was constructed around the grave to mark the location and keep livestock away. A proper headstone was never erected.

John took his brother's journals and other valuables from the cabin and the building was abandoned forever. Cass Hite's old black hat was still hanging on a peg amid the ruins of the cabin many years later.

In Salt Lake City, a single paragraph summed up the life of Hosteen Pish-la-ki:

The Salt Lake Mining Review
March 15, 1914

Cass Hite, an old time prospector of Colorado and Utah, died February 16 in his cabin on the Colorado River, near Hite, Utah. Mr. Hite was 69 years old and has prospected in this section for the past forty years, being largely interested in placer gold diggings on the Colorado. He is survived by his brother, John P. Hite, of Hite, Utah, and a nephew, Ben G. [Homer] Hite of Salt Lake, mining editor of the Salt Lake Evening Telegram.

Cass Hite's grave at Ticaboo – 1938
Courtesy of Utah State Historical Society

The Trail for Sixty Snows

In March 1905, Cass Hite turned sixty-years-old. It was an unexpected milestone for him, and to celebrate he wrote an epic poem about his life. Undoubtedly, the poetry of Cy Warman was his inspiration. When Warman wrote "The Ghost of Hoskininni" while staying at Dandy Crossing, Cass was very impressed.

At his little cabin in Ticaboo, Cass worked on his literary endeavor for several weeks. He wrote and re-wrote, struggling to express his innermost feelings while striving to maintain a proper veneer of "strong Western manhood."

With no wife or posterity to keep his memory alive, Cass knew this poem and his journals might be the only testament of his life to survive him.

The Trail of Hosteen Pish-La-Ki for Sixty Snows

Cass Hite was born on the 3rd of March
Eighteen and forty-five,
Full sixty snows have fell since then
And finds him still alive.

Seven hundred and twenty moons,
Sweet Regent of the Sky,
Has righteously shone on the trail
Of Hosteen Pish-la-ki.

For three-score snows he blazed the trail
From infancy to age,
The story might not fill a book
But maybe so a page.

The many scenes and incidents
And sorrows of that time,
He cannot properly relate
In ordinary rhyme.

The first ten snows were on a farm
In the Old Prairie state,
The happiest in all his life
Right bang up to date.

The first momentous incident
In all those early years,
Was when his father went away
And left us all in tears.

To California after gold
He surely was in line,
An Argonaut they then were called
In eighteen forty-nine.

And well do we remember when
We sang a merry song,
And did our very level best
To get to go along.

Mother opposed his notion then
He remembers what she said,
Cass, you shut up your cryin' now
Get on that trundle bed.

Father's going far away
In quest of yellow gold,
You stay at home – you are too small
You're only four years old.

How often he has wanted since
That little trundle bed,
When out in storms a prospecting
Nowhere to lay his head.

A climbing in the mountains
He remembers he was told
By his good mother long ago
When he was four years old.

Ah! Those were truly joyful days
He didn't know it then,
But many times he's thought so since
Wherever he has been.

And when he lived his next four snows
In famous Salem town,
That did proclaim some intellect
Of national renown.

Warmouth, Merrit and Bryon
All soared away up high,
And to complete the galaxy
Was Hosteen Pish-la-ki.

The last, not least, of them four stars
To the printing office went.
To get some learning in his head
And be an ornament.

For one full snow he stuck up type
And carried papers round
To patrons of the "Advocate"
That lived within the town.

But father found another job
He didn't mean no harm,
He put H. Pish-La-Ki to work
Down on the bottom farm.

There were nine children of us then
In early morn did rise,
Seven of us still remain
Two in the churchyard lies.

The older children were away
Some of them off to school
And Hosteen Pish-la-ki at work
Was generally the rule.

And with his industrious traits
He developed – what do you think
An extensive admiration for
Dances and strong drink.

The good and bad in some of us
Is sadly jumbled up,
And he declares he can't see why
Life's such a bitter cup.

And a strange infatuation
Seized him in those early days
That made the cup more bitter
Than all his other ways.

Gambling was the worst of all
The faults that he possessed,
And the devil seemed to glorify
When he was most distressed.

But all those ailments disappeared
And still he is alive,
He drew the line both hard and fast
At the age of fifty-five.

A little late, he does admit
And makes a sorry tale,
Unfortunately he found it
While he was blazing trail.

And on that trial of sixty snows
He had a certain trend
To ascertain who were his foes,
And sometimes who his friend.

The span of life upon the farm
While he was in his teens
Was full of pleasant, joyful days,
He remembers by all means.

But Hosteen Pish-la-ki lit out
At the age of twenty-one,
To the mountains in the distant west
Toward the setting sun.

Twas in the sixties he did wend
His way across the plains,
Thru buffalo and antelope
Thru sunshine and thru rains.

He surely did enjoy his life
In the great and glorious west,
And he held his own, the best he could
And did his level best.

When first he saw the snowy range
A towering to the sky,
It put great life in the humble form
Of Hosteen Pish-la-ki.

He thought of the stories his father told
And the way he told them were fine,
About the journey across the plains
In eighteen forty-nine.

Three snows and a half he rambled west
In that cold snowy zone,
That covers the various streams that form
The Missouri and Yellowstone.

And on the Salmon in Idaho
He pursued his search for gold,
But the climate was too hard for him
Twas all together too cold.

He wasn't exactly homesick then
But studied the case all around,
He wanted to see a girl back yon
And he was homeward bound.

To old Missouri he went that time
Well satisfied to roam,
In civilization just a spell
And to visit the folks at home.

He enjoyed himself for about four snows
But prospered not the best,
The spirit to roam was ripe in him
And again he ambled west.

The Missouri River he bade goodbye
In the spring of seventy-four,
And crossed the plains the second time
To the snowy range once more.

For seven snows he led the life
Of a mining prospector,
The trail was generally smooth enough
But sometimes there was war.

He discovered some famous mines
That went way up to the ton,
And the largest natural bridge on earth
In the head of White Canyon.

Cliff dweller ruins he explored
In the land of the Navajo,
Where the pale face never set his foot
Arizona and Mexico.

In the autumn of eighteen eighty-one
He went to great Utah,
And for twenty-four snows he will now relate
A few of the things he saw.

He got his outfit all in line
With four comrades to go,
Down upon the Rio San Juan
In the land of the Navajo.

To hunt for the Indian mine, they said
That ran away up high,
And was called by the wiley Navajo
El Mino Pesso-la-ki

For two full snows he followed that trail
And many chances took,
But the Navajo outwitted him
By every hook and crook.

He gave it up and blazed the trail
To the Colorado Grand,
A great old river of the west
That carried golden sand.

The great Glen Canyon, it runs through
With rapids wild and bold,
That cuts the great strata of time
Sixteen million years old.

Majestic walls that there surround
A towering to the sky,
Guards Ticaboo the place where lives
Old Hosteen Pish-la-ki.

Old Hoskininni is the chief
Of the Western Navajo,
Old Hosteen Pish-la-ki's his friend
He says that it is so.

A tale was written years ago
By a poet of national note
The Ghost of Hoskininni was
By great Cy Warman wrote.

Old Hosteen Pish-la-ki's for peace
And mostly shuns his foes,
But when no other way will work
Is sometimes bellicose.

A most unfortunate event
Occurred in ninety-one,
Up at Green River in Utah
Just at the set of sun.

A gang of toughs tried to slay him
A death struggle ensued,
And with the first law of nature
He was strongly imbued.

In mortal combat he engaged
It's sad the story goes,
He played his hand the best he could
And down sure went his foes.

You ask if he's not sorry for
The deplorable affair,
For being compelled to do it he
Most certainly does care.

The very great old Count Tolstoy
Does non-resistance talk,
And though it were to save his life
He'd rather take a walk.

But Hosteen Pish-la-ki is weak
He's been that way from birth,
He don't know about that other world
And is satisfied on earth.

No logic or philosophy
Exempts a man from fight,
Or to defend himself when he
Is surely in the right.

And as the snows fall on the trail
With the Reagent of the Sky,
More peaceful thoughts possess the soul
Of Hosteen Pish-la-ki

And in his home at Ticaboo
He built with his own hand,
He's got a garden and a bank
And happiest in the land.

In Hanksville Town lives his best girl
Who made a lovely tie,
To circumnavigate the neck
Of Hosteen Pish-la-ki

And they write letters back and forth
'Bout once a month or so,
And the fun they have is sure good stuff
He'd have them all to know.

Maggie writes H. Pish-La-Ki
The news from Hanksville Town,
'Bout how they cuss and cuss and cuss
But generally laugh it down.

This tickles Hosteen Pish-la-ki
And he writes to Marguerite,
'Bout the great big fish at Ticaboo
And the grapes and melons sweet.

Majestic walls that there surround
A towering to the sky,
That place at Ticaboo where lives
Old Hosteen Pish-la-ki

He tells her of his old Tom Cat,
His Injun horse and Bill
That good for nothing mean black colt
That's only fit to kill.

And how he takes his fiddle down
When he is all alone,
To skeer the sly coyotes away
A sawin' a frightful tune.

He tries his hand at playing a waltz
Arkansas Traveler, too,
And the echoes ring around the walls
That surround Ticaboo.

He tires to play home sweet home
But finds it no good scheme,
Changes the tune, quickens the beat
And flies at the devils dream.

Pats time with his foot to keep the beat
And thinks as he plays away,
He'll try to help the fiddle out
By singing "Maggie May."

Gets action on both string and voice
And doesn't miss a note,
And kicks up such a terrible din
He skeers the wild coyote.

Old Hosteen Pish-la-ki has been
Considered derelict,
In not joining the wedding throng
And became a Benedict.

But he's not altogether to blame
For the single life he's spent,
The ladies, more than one, he says
Have had his full consent.

And Hosteen Pish-la-ki has seen
Some different degrees,
Of wedded life that puzzles him
The more of it he sees.

In Washington's farewell address
Some good advice he gave,
From entangling alliances
His countrymen to save.

His warning was most statesmen like
And through this age it rings,
And if it then was good it might
Be good in other things.

Alliances are multiform
In character we know,
Some are made for purest love
And some are made for dough.

Some result in greatest bliss
And some in sad despair,
But Washington did surely say
My countrymen, Beware.

This Hosteen Pish-la-ki did drink
Strong stuff for forty snows,
And he tells you that it did bring
Those ailments known as woes.

Five snows ago he quit the bad
He thought he had the pluck,
To hit the trail a sober tack
Which brought him best of luck.

The sixty moons brought back his health
And friends he had galore,
And he's concluded to start in
And give it five snows more.

And when he calculates to live
For at least thirty years,
Before he's called upon to quit
This pleasant vale of tears.

He hopes to live beyond that time
When Gabriel's trumpet blows,
For he has got a solid hunch
On all of thirty snows.

Epilogue

The post office at Hite was closed in 1914, a few months after Cass died. The store died with it and John moved back to Missouri. The journals Cass had so carefully kept over the years are thought to have been lost when John's house in St. Louis burned down.

Sometime in the 1930s, someone set fire to Cass Hite's old cabin at Ticaboo and only the rock chimney survived. Some of the grape vines lived into the 1960s and river runners refreshed themselves on fruit Cass Hite had planted.

In 1934 Cass got a neighbor in his little fenced graveyard at Ticaboo. John W. Dehlin had come to the river in 1933 with his sons to prospect for gold. John knew he had stomach cancer, and he stayed in the canyons until he died, telling his boys to bury him there by Cass Hite at Ticaboo. One wonders what the hermit of Ticaboo, old Hosteen Pish-la-ki, would have had to say about that.

In 1939, Charles Kelly interviewed Hoskininni Begay in Monument Valley. The old Navajo, about 80 years old at the time, gave him valuable information about Cass Hite, Hoskininni, and the lost Mitchell and Merrick Mine.

Indian Joe, Cass Hite's Paiute companion, guide, and consultant on all things Native American, disappears from the literature after 1885. What happened to him is not known.

The farm at Hite passed through several owners until 1932. Then Arthur Chaffin, a miner who had worked the gold bars on the river as a boy in the 1890s, returned and bought the place. Chaffin made several improvements to the property and borrowed heavy equipment from Garfield County to make the first road through North Wash suitable for automobiles. In 1946 he constructed a ferryboat at Hite, using World War II surplus pontoon boats with an old Model A Ford for an engine. The ferry was known as the Chaffin Ferry, or the Hite Ferry.

The uranium boom brought a measure of prosperity to the region, and in 1949 a uranium mill was constructed across the river from Hite in the shadow of Fort Moki. A little town grew up around the mill called White Canyon. The town had almost 200 residents by 1952 and sported a store, post office, airstrip and one-room schoolhouse. The mill was closed in 1954 and the town died.

River running became a popular pastime after the Second World War and several groups passed through Hite and Ticaboo on their way through Glen Canyon, stopping to explore the ruins of the gold operations and the old cabin sites. The Stanton dredge became a famous junk pile along the river near Bullfrog Creek. In 1938 Julius Stone, the former president of Stanton's Hoskininni Mining Company, stopped at the shipwreck with a group on a river tour of the canyons. The party pulled a few boards from the wreck to kindle a fire for coffee. As Julius surveyed the wreckage with his coffee cup in hand, he told the others that this one cup of hot coffee was the only return he ever got for his $5,000 investment. Undoubtedly, there were many similar stories told by other men of means who had invested heavily in the Glen Canyon gold rush.

Cass Hite's friend and neighbor, Bert Loper, was lost to the river in 1949 and his body was never found. Loper had gone to float the Grand Canyon to celebrate his 80th birthday. When his boat capsized in a rapid, Loper, who was wearing a lifejacket, was washed away downstream and was never seen again. A monument to the old pioneer river runner stands in the city park in Green River, Utah.

Alonzo Turner died while working his gold claims at the California Bar in 1923 and was buried in Hanksville. Well-meaning friends erected a small cement monument, with his name misspelled, near his old rock cabin on the river. In 1964 his memorial was covered by Lake Powell.

In 1956 Congress passed the Colorado River Storage Project and the Glen Canyon Dam became a reality. The first concrete was poured at the site in 1960. The floodgates were closed in 1963 and the muddy water began backing up through Glen Canyon.

The Hite Ferry made her last run on June 5, 1964. By the end of July the water had covered the ferry site, farm, and Cass Hite's old log cabin. At full capacity, Lake Powell is 200 feet deep over Dandy Crossing.

Two modern bridges span the Dirty Devil and Colorado Rivers about five miles upstream from Dandy Crossing. The confluence of the Dirty Devil and Colorado Rivers marks the official top end of Glen Canyon and Lake Powell. A marina and boat ramp were constructed near the highway bridges and given the name Hite. The Hite Marina is along highway 95, across the lake from the Wrinkle Rocks at the mouth of North Wash.

In the late 1970s a uranium mill was constructed at the west end of Ticaboo Mesa along Utah state highway 276, about 10 air-miles southwest of Cass Hite's grave. A small, unincorporated town named Ticaboo was established near the mill. The mill closed after only a few years, but remnants of the town survive. The place is known today as the Ticaboo Resort.

No one has ever found Hoskininni's silver, nor has The Lost Rhoades Mine of the Uintah Mountains ever been discovered.

For fifty years Cass Hite slept peacefully in the warm sand of Ticaboo, but in 1964 the cold water touched his gravesite. The ruins of his old home, garden, and life were fully inundated before the year was out.

They say at midnight when the winds
From out of the canyons blow,
And Lake Powell's foamy waves
Dash on the rocks below.

When moonlight fills the canyons
And stars glisten in the sky,
Ride the ghosts of Hoskininni
And Hosteen Pish-la-ki.

Acknowledgments:

Thank you to Jo Anne Chandler, Gladys May, and the staff at the Green River Archives in Green River, Utah, who took an interest in this project and provided valuable information, maps and photographs from their files.

Thank you to Steve Allen, Ron Noyes, Cleal Bradford, and Jack and Melba Winn, some of the people who provided information used in this book.

A special thank you to Jeannie, my pretty wife, who offered encouragement and read the first draft of every chapter, fearlessly acting as literary critic and editor of first resort. A good woman is more precious than pearls, especially one willingly to spend days and weeks on the desert in search of history and hidden outlaw trails.

Other books by Tom McCourt:

The Split Sky: A Journey of Discovery in Utah's Nine Mile Canyon

White Canyon: Remembering the Little Town at the Bottom of Lake Powell

To Be a Soldier

Cowpokes to Bike Spokes: The Story of Moab, Utah

Last of the Robber's Roost Outlaws: Moab's Bill Tibbetts

To order books, contact Tom McCourt at Southpaw Publications:
    435-637-4544
    southpaw@emerytelcom.net

Endnotes:

Hoskininni's Silver

Page 11 James Merrick and Ernest Mitchell: There is some confusion about the first names of Merrick and Mitchell. Three or four possibilities are given in various texts. For this book, the names used are the names recorded by Martin Clark Powell in his thesis: A Study and Historical Analysis of the Document, "The Trail of Hosteen Pish-La-Ki for Sixty Snows," University of Redlands, 1963. The Harry Alison Papers, University of Utah Marriott Library, Special Collections.

Undefeated

Page 14 Hoskininni's silver: Charles Kelly, "Chief Hoskininni," Blue Mountain Shadows, The Magazine of San Juan County History, volume 12, Summer 1993. Reprinted by permission from Utah State Historical Quarterly, Vol. 21, July 1953. Hoskininni Begay testified that there is a lost Navajo silver mine. Though just a boy at the time, he said he saw the silver his father brought to the Indian camp.

Across the River

Page 16 boundaries of the Navajo Reservation: The San Juan River became the official northern boundary of the reservation in 1884.

Page 17 Rabbit Ears John: Paul Schurtz, Millard County Chronicle, January 23, 1941. The account presented in this book follows the newspaper article. However, in this book, the story of Rabbit Ears John is plausible fiction. It seems improbable that Mitchell and Merrick could have found the Navajo silver so quickly and easily in hostile territory without a guide. Reason suggests that a Navajo took them there.

Page 18 Grandpa Peter Schurtz: Ron McDonald, "Fort Montezuma," Blue Mountain Shadows Magazine, Volume 30, Summer 2004. Peter Schurtz Sr. was a Mormon Elder who often corresponded with Brigham Young. In spite of his advanced age, in 1877 he was the first pioneer to settle along the San Juan River.

Page 18 Cass Hite volunteered to join the search: Paul Schurtz, Millard County Chronicle, January 23, 1941. This account places Cass Hite at Mitchell's Trading Post as the search for the lost prospectors began.

The Valley of Tears

Page 19 we lost another boy, Mother: Paul Schurtz, Millard County Chronicle, January 23, 1941. The story of the search party follows closely this newspaper account, including the homecoming and Mrs. Mitchell's words and behavior.

Page 20 James Merrick is still out there: Mitchell and Merrick Buttes in Monument Valley are named for the murdered prospectors. The men were killed near there.

Into the Wilderness Dream

Page 21 in the footsteps of his father: Cass Hite, *The Trail of Hosteen Pish-La-Ki for Sixty Snows,* an autobiographical poem written in 1905. The Harry Alison Papers, University of Utah Marriott Library, Special Collections. Information about Levi Hite comes form The Salt Lake Tribune, September 13, 1891. The story says Levi Hite was a California gold miner and a prominent merchant in Gold Hill, Nevada, having passed away in 1866, the year Cass went west for the first time.

Page 21 an epic poem he wrote about his life: Cass Hite, *The Trail of Hosteen Pish-La-Ki for Sixty Snows.*

Page 21 Cass showed up on the San Juan River in 1879: In his poem, Cass says he went to Utah in 1881. However, Paul Schurtz places him on the San Juan at Mitchell's Trading Post, in Utah Territory, in January, 1880. Also, Cass Hite's brother, Ben Hite, is quoted in a newspaper article, Salt Lake Tribune, January 4, 1893, as saying that Cass was "with" Mitchell and Merrick "before" they were killed by Indians in January 1880.

Page 21 Ruben Turner described Cass Hite: Ruben Turner, Millard County Chronicle, May 5, 1932.

Page 21 Cass Hite's education: Cass Hite, *The Trail of Hosteen Pish-La-Ki for Sixty Snows.* Cass said some of his siblings went to school while he had to work on the farm. His tone seems resentful. The only education he claims for himself was setting type for a newspaper. He does, however, list himself among "a galaxy of renowned scholars" including William Jennings Bryan.

Page 22 Cass carried a cut-off revolver and shot from the hip: Arthur Chaffin interview with P.T. Reilly, 1966. Green River Archives, Green river, Utah.

Page 22 Cass shot a man in Colorado: Martin Clark Powell thesis, Harry Alison Papers, University of Utah Marriott Library, Special Collections, Page 19. A letter from Frank Beckwith to Charles Kelly quotes Cass Hite as saying, "I shot the whole g-- d--- hip out of a son-of-a-b---- in Colorado."

Page 22 duels were a thing of the past: Martin Clark Powell, page 19, note 18. Arthur Chaffin related the story to Powell as told to him by Alonzo (Lon) Turner, one of the early Glen Canyon prospectors. Lon is the man who found Cass Hite dead in 1914. Though they shared a common last name and were on the Colorado at the same time, Lon Turner and Ruben Turner were not relatives.

Moonlight Canyon

Page 26 Moonlight Canyon: On the map drawn by Cass Hite in 1891, he places Moonlight Canyon one canyon east of Copper Canyon. Today that canyon is known as Piute Farms Wash.

Page 28 Injun Joe: Several accounts tell of Cass Hite having an Indian guide. Some say the man was a Paiute. "Indian Joe" is listed as a member of Cass Hite's party when the natural bridges were discovered in December 1883, as told by The Salt Lake Telegram, February 4, 1917.

Page 30 the first oil discovery in Southern Utah: Charles Goodman, Salt Lake Mining Review, April 15, 1910. Headline, "History of the Oil Fields in San Juan County."

Hosteen Pish-La-Ki

Page 30 The old chief: Charles Kelly, "Chief Hoskininni," Blue Mountain Shadows Magazine, Volume 12, Summer 1993. In his interview with Charles Kelly, Hoskininni Begay said he was 20 years old when Cass Hite first came to the Indian camp. Cass Hite would have been 36, and Hoskininni, "the old chief," might have been in his early 70s. Arthur Chaffin, who knew Hoskininni, said in an interview with P.T. Reilly in 1966 that Hoskininni was 100-years-old when he died in 1909.

Page 33 Quantrill's Raiders: Possibly the most authoritative source of information about Quantrill's Raiders comes from the book, "Gray Ghosts of the Confederacy" by Richard Brownlee, University of Louisiana Press, 1958. In his book, Mr. Brownlee lists all of the men known to have served with Quantrill's Raiders. Cass Hite is not on that list, nor is any other man named Hite. However, a man named Robert W. Hite is listed as having served with Captain William (Bloody Bill) Anderson of the Missouri Partisan Rangers, a rebel guerilla unit closely associated with Quantrill. Robert Hite was killed shortly after the war while robbing trains with Jesse James.

Page 34 Cass returned the items to Henry Mitchell: Paul Schurtz letter to Charles Kelly dated June 22, 1940. Schurtz said Cass Hite recovered almost all of the property belonging to Mitchell and Merrick and returned it to Henry Mitchell.

Page 35 Cass stayed at the Navajo camp for a year and a half: Charles Kelly, Blue Mountain Shadows Magazine, Volume 12, Summer 1993. In the interview, Hoskininni Begay said Cass came to the Indian camp in 1881 and stayed all summer. Then he came back in 1882 and stayed again, "for a long time." Since Cass didn't arrive at Dandy Crossing until mid-1883, he probably spent 12 to 20 months living with the Navajos.

Page 35 Cass planned to marry an Indian woman: Paul Schurtz letter to Charles Kelly dated July 26, 1940. Charles Kelly Collection, Utah State Historical Society.

Page 36 Blood brothers: Charles Kelly, Blue Mountain Shadows Magazine, Volume 12, Summer 1993. In the interview, Hoskininni Begay said he and Cass became blood brothers. Nowhere does Cass talk about this.

It is not in his autobiographical poem and the author is unaware of Cass or his brothers ever mentioning this in any of their correspondence or newspaper interviews. Perhaps the idea of mixing blood with an Indian during a heathen ritual was considered barbaric by proper Victorian society and Cass was not apt to mention it.

Page 36 you are Hosteen Pish-La-Ki: The name in Navajo is pronounced, "Hastquin, besh lagai. "Hastquin" means "mister," and "besh lagai" means white metal, or silver. In English, Hosteen Pish-la-ki comes close to the original Navajo, with "ki" sounding like "ky" in the word sky. Also, in Navajo, the term Hastquin (Hawsteen) (Hosteen) means more than simply mister. It is a term that carries more respect. As time went by, Cass became very proud of his Navajo name. He used it often, sometimes signing his name as Hosteen Pish-la-ki.

The Spaniards Yellow Gold

Page 39 Moki (or Moqui): In the 1700s and early 1800s, both the Spanish and early Anglo explorers called the pueblo Indians "Moquis," a name given them by the Utes. The term was also used to denote the ancient cliff dwellers of the four corners area. After the Pecos Archaeological Conference of 1927, the Navajo term "Anasazi" became universally accepted and most people stopped using the term Moki.

Page 39 Trachyte Creek: Trachyte is an igneous, volcanic rock. Trachyte Canyon was named by the John Wesley Powell river survey of 1871. Powell also named the Henry Mountains after Joseph Henry, the first secretary of the Smithsonian Institution. The Henry Mountains were the last major mountain chain to be added to the maps of the continental United States.

Page 40 Spanish mines in Glen Canyon: Cy Warman, Aspen Daily Chronicle, April 27, 1893. "It was here [Ticaboo] where Cass Hite found the old Spanish workings, as he had been told he would find them, by Hoskininni, the Navajo." Cy Warman got the story directly from Cass Hite. One of the unanswered questions about Hoskininni showing Cass there was gold along the river has been; how did the Indians know there was gold there? The gold is "flour gold," so fine it cannot be seen until it shows up as yellow silt in the bottom of a gold pan. A Navajo memory of Spaniards digging gold from the river sand answers the question perfectly.

Page 40 Ticaboo Canyon. It is not known who named Ticaboo Canyon. It was probably Cass Hite since he was the first and only pioneer to settle there.

Page 40 Iron Hat Mexicans: Cy Warman wrote a famous poem, "The Ghost of Hoskininni." In it he says: "For there it was the Spaniard / He said made injun slave / And maybeso the river / Flows sometimes by the grave / Of my own mother's mother / Who 'fore she came to die / Was made to dig the peso / For the Hosteen Pish-la-ki." This undoubtedly came from the Spanish mine story Hoskininni told Cass Hite. If Warman's information is correct, the story tells about Hoskininni's grandmother and the event would date in the mid to late 1700s and not the 1680 Pueblo Revolt as some have suggested.

Dandy Crossing

Page 41 the gold dust had a yellow sheen: Cy Warman, Aspen Daily Chronicle, April 27, 1893. Warman said gold from the Henry Mountains was red in color, but the Colorado River gold was a beautiful yellow.

The Wild Man of Swett Canyon

Page 45 Joshua Swett: Gregory Crampton, University of Utah Anthropological Papers, Number 72, August 1964, Page 38. In an interview with Arthur Chaffin in 1960, Chaffin said the first white man to live in the Dandy Crossing area was a squaw man and horse thief named Joshua Swett. The man had a cabin at the mouth of Swett Canyon as early as 1872. Chaffin said Swett left the area after Cass Hite showed up. The Salt Lake Tribune, September 26, 1884 said Joshua Swett was sentenced to three years in prison for grand theft – probably horse stealing.

Wonders of the Desert

Page 54 Little Bridge was re-christened Edwin Bridge: Salt Lake Telegram, February 4, 1917. Headline: "Scenic Wonders Found in Southern Utah."

The Fight at Soldier Crossing

Page 55 The Fight at Soldier Crossing: Winston Hurst and Robert McPherson, "The Fight at Solder Crossing" Blue Mountain Shadows Magazine, volume 29, Winter 2004. This chapter paraphrases Hurst and McPherson's account of the battle.

Page 56 no settlements near Blue Mountain at the time: The town of Monticello was founded in 1888. Grayson (Blanding) in 1905.

Page 60 Piute Pass: The proper modern spelling is "Paiute." That is how the Paiute Tribe of Utah is listed on their official website. In years past, the name was often spelled "Piute." It is still that way on most Utah maps and there is a Piute County, Utah.

Gold Rush in Glen Canyon

Page 62 placer claims along the river had not been his first choice: There are two traditional ways to mine gold, placer mining and lode mining. Lode mining is when a tunnel or shaft is bored to find and follow a vein of ore. Placer mining is surface mining done on sand and gravel deposits along ancient streambeds to recover gold deposited by erosion. Placer gold is "washed" from the dirt using a gold pan or sluice box.

Page 63 Cass Hite is a horse's ass: On a sandstone pioneer register in today's Capital Reef National Park, the inscription says: "Theodore Christensen, prospector, Gunnison Utah, Henry Mountain or bust." Nearby is written, "Busted by God." Near that is the name "Cass Hite" and a crudely drawn picture of a man's face and a horse's behind.

Page 65 Eagle City and the Bromide Basin Mine: In about 1900 the mineshafts began filling with water. The ore-processing mill burned down in 1911. Lacking capital to properly drain the water and rebuild the mill, the company slowly went out of business. By 1917 Eagle City was a ghost town. A hermit, Frank Lawler, lived there until the 1970s. The mine has never reopened.

Page 65 ferry service at Dandy Crossing: In The Salt Lake Tribune, July 12, 1890, Cass Hite said he owned a ferry at Dandy Crossing. In the Ogden Standard Examiner, January 13, 1893, Ben Hite also said there was ferry service there. In spite of those claims, the author is unaware of any pictures or first-hand accounts of a ferry operated by the Hite brothers. The crude boats or rafts made from cottonwood logs might have been the only ferry they ever had.

King of the Colorado

Page 68 Cass had a way of gathering men around him: Ruben Turner, unpublished manuscript in possession of the author courtesy of Ron Noyes.

Page 68 The newspaper article paraphrased here appeared in the Salt Lake Tribune, July 12, 1890. There might be a story behind Cass Hite saying he hated Mormon Elders as he did a rattlesnake, but what might have passed between him and the Mormons is not known. There are no specific incidents in the literature, other than Cass Hite's statements of conflict and hatred. If Mormon "Avenging Angels" really did try to kill him, he doesn't mention it in any of his writings.

Page 69 The Grand River: The upper Colorado River, from the headwaters to the confluence with the Green River, was known as the Grand River until 1921. The name was changed by an act of congress.

The Angel of Mercy

Page 74 buggy ride to Hanksville: Millard County Chronicle, May 5, 1932. Unfortunately, the year the young man took a very sick Cass Hite to Hanksville is not specified, and that has caused confusion. Some sources say Cass was near death when released from prison in 1893, but newspaper stories tell otherwise. Evidently, Cass had two bouts of near-fatal illness, the first about 1890 and the second in 1900. The 1890 incident is described here.

Page 78 she was looking forward to the blessed event: Folklore, rumors and ancient small town gossip suggests that Cass Hite fathered an out-of-wedlock child with a widow lady in Hanksville who nursed him back to health. Strong credence is lent to the truthfulness of the story by the fact that Cass, by his own admission, had a special relationship with a little girl in Hanksville named Maggie. Cass tells about Maggie in his epic poem. The story of Maggie and her mother has been woven into this narrative, but names have been changed to protect the innocent.

Mining Men's Pockets

Page 80 the trouble between Cass Hite and Adolph Kohler: Arthur Chaffin, Interview with P.T. Reilly, 1966. Green River Archives, Green River, Utah.

Unjustified Justifiable Homicide

Page 85 the gunfight in Green River: Events of the gunfight are from testimony given at Cass Hite's murder trials, as reported by several newspapers.

Cass Hite Brought Hither

Page 88 Cass Hite's interview at the Marshal's office: Paraphrased from The Salt Lake Tribune, October 14, 1891.

Page 89 bail was set at $20,000. Twenty thousand dollars would be the equivalent of half-a-million at today's rates, maybe a little more.

Liars, Lawyers, and a Lack of Luck

Page 91 Cass went back to Colorado to raise more money: The Daily Enquirer, September 25, 1892.

Keep the Home Fires Burning:

Page 95 Cy Warman, a reliable source: Warman's information about the value of Colorado River placers was published in the Aspen Daily Chronicle, April 27, 1893.

Enoch Davis and the Lost Rhoades Mine

Page 100 Thomas Rhoades: Thomas Rhoades died in Minersville, Utah in 1869. He had four wives and thirty-six children.

Page 100 the Mormon Battalion: The Mormon Battalion was formed in 1846 as part of the U.S. army. Their mission was to help win the Mexican-American War. The unit was made up of 500 Mormon volunteers recruited near Council Bluffs, Iowa. They marched to California via New

Mexico and Arizona without engaging any Mexicans. The battalion was disbanded in California and former members of the unit, working for Mr. Sutter, were the first to find gold in California in 1848.

Page 100 Caleb Rhoades: Caleb Rhoades was the son of Thomas Rhoades and his first wife, Elizabeth Forster, who died in California. Caleb was born in 1836 and died in 1905. He was 57 years old and living in Price, Utah when Enoch Davis and Cass Hite were conspiring to find the mine in 1893.

Page 100 the State of Deseret: Utah Territory was originally known as "Deseret" or "The State of Deseret." The name was bestowed by the early Mormon leadership. Deseret is a word from the Book of Mormon meaning "honeybee." The name implied industry and orderliness. In 1850 the State of Deseret became Utah Territory by an act of congress. A beehive is still the centerpiece of the Utah State Seal and "Industry" the state motto.

Page 101 Indians found them there and Enoch Rhoades was killed: According to LDS (Mormon) genealogy records, Enoch Rhoades was the son of Thomas Rhoades and plural wife Jacobine Jorgensen. He was born in 1861 and died in 1884. The place and cause of his death is not listed. Enoch Davis and others said he was killed by Indians on the Uintah Mountains.

Page 102 Colonel Montgomery came through in spades: The Salt Lake Tribune, October 30, 1893, "Cass Hite Receives Pardon."

Expedition to the Uintahs

Page 106 The Lost Rhoades Mine found: Vernal Express, June 14, 1894. The newspaper story is different from the story Enoch Davis told Cass Hite and the Salt Lake Tribune. Lorenzo Hatch claimed to have a brother who was a partner with Enoch Davis when the mine was found in 1885. Davis never mentioned that. It is interesting that, in the Lorenzo Hatch account, no mention is made of Enoch Rhoades who was the leader of the expedition, had the original map to the mine, and was killed by Indians shortly after the mine was found. The discrepancy remains a mystery.

Page 113 the Enoch Davis execution: The Salt Lake Herald and the Salt Lake Tribune, September 15, 1894.

The Salt Lake City Gold Rush

Page 119 the Oquirrh Mountains: Oquirrh is said to be a Ute Indian word meaning "shining."

Page 119 the Bingham Canyon mines: Gold was discovered in Bingham Canyon, about seven miles south of Harker's Canyon in the 1860s. Gold mining was undertaken there with limited success for several years. Copper proved to be the dominant mineral and the Kennecott Copper, Bingham Canyon Mine was opened in 1904. Today the Bingham Canyon Mine is one of the world's largest open pit mines.

The Long Road Back to Dandy Crossing

Page 124 Cass sent Indians to buy whiskey: Charles Kelly, "Chief Hoskininni," Blue Mountain Shadows Magazine, Volume 12, Summer 1993. At the time, this was highly unusual and probably illegal.

Stanton's Folly

Page 133 A brief account of Robert Stanton's gold dredge can be found in the book *Ghosts of Glen Canyon* by C. Gregory Crampton. More detailed information is available on the Internet.

Old Dogs Still Bite

Page 143 the young man and the rowdy drunk: Ruben Turner, unpublished manuscript in possession of the author courtesy of Ron Noyes. Turner said the incident happened in 1904. Cass Hite would have been 59 years old.

The Ghosts of Glen Canyon

Page 149 Cy Warman's Poem, "The Ghost of Hoskininni." Warman obviously interpreted the meaning of the name, "Hosteen Pish-La-ki" to mean someone or something evil. In his 11-stanza poem, three times he has the ghost of Hoskininni guarding against, or blocking the pathway, of "the Hosteen Pish-La-ki." One stanza tells of Hosininni's grandmother "made to dig the peso for the Hosteen Pish-La-ki." Warman was clearly using the term to portray the Spaniards "he said made injun slave." Either Warman was misinformed about the meaning of the term, or Cass Hite's Indian name had a different connotation than what we think today. In the context of the poem, "Mr. Silver" makes no sense. Warman wrote the poem in 1893 while Cass was in prison. Had Cass been able to collaborate with the poet before the poem was published, he might have suggested some changes. In spite of that, Cass was very proud when Warman's poem was circulated nationally and made his Navajo name famous.

Page 150 Bert Loper and Cass Hite: Brad Dimock, "The Very Hard Way: Bert Loper and the Colorado River," Fretwater Press, Flagstaff Arizona, 2007.

Page 152 Cass Hite's burial: Details of finding Cass dead and his burial at Ticaboo were told by Ruben Turner in several of his writings and newspaper interviews.

The Trail of Hosteen Pish-La-Ki for Sixty Snows

Page 154 There are three known versions of the poem, each a little different from the others. It seems the poem was reworked over a period of years with improvements to the words, meter and rhyme.

Page 159 Cass found the largest natural bridge in the world: That statement was true when the poem was written in 1905. Rainbow Bridge, which is larger, wasn't discovered until 1909.

Epilogue

Page 165 Julius Stone at the ruins of the Stanton dredge: Gregory C. Crampton, *The Ghosts of Glen Canyon*. Cricket Productions, Salt Lake City, Utah, 1994.

Page 167 The figures at the bottom of the page were copied from Ute petroglyphs on the sandstone walls of Utah's Nine Mile Canyon.